Grazing management

Longman Handbooks in Agriculture

Series editors

C. T. Whittemore
K. Simpson

Books published

C. T. Whittemore: *Pig production – the scientific and practical principles*
A. W. Speedy: *Sheep production – science into practice*
R. H. F. Hunter: *Reproduction of farm animals*
K. Simpson: *Soil*
J. D. Leaver: *Milk production – science and practice*
J. M. Wilkinson: *Beef production from silage and other conserved forages*
E. Farr and W. C. Henderson: *Land drainage*
K. Simpson: *Fertilizers and manures*
C. T. Whittemore: *Elements of pig science*

Grazing Management
Science into Practice

John Hodgson

Professor of Agronomy,
Massey University, Palmerston North,
New Zealand

Longman
Scientific &
Technical

Copublished in the United States with
John Wiley & Sons, Inc., New York

Longman Scientific & Technical,
Longman Group UK Ltd,
Longman House, Burnt Mill, Harlow,
Essex CM20 2JE, England
and associated Companies throughout the world.

Copublished in the United States with
John Wiley & Sons, Inc., 605 Third Avenue, New York,
NY 10158

First published 1990

British Library Cataloguing in Publication Data
Hodgson, John
  Grazing management.
  1. Livestock. Grazing
  I. Title
  636.08′4

  ISBN 0-582-45010-1

Library of Congress Cataloging-in-Publication Data
Hodgson, John G.
    Grazing management: science into practice/John Hodgson.
      p.   cm. – (Longman handbooks in agriculture)
    Includes bibliographical references.
    ISBN 0-470-21644-1 (Wiley)
    1. Grazing – Management.   2. Range management.
    3. Grazing – Environmental aspects.   I. Title. II. Series.
    SF85.H53   1990   89-13742
    633.2′02 – dc20   CIP

Set in Linotron 202 10/12pt Times Roman

Produced by Longman Group (FE) Limited
Printed in Hong Kong

Contents

In memory of my father, Dick Hodgson,
who used to pose the questions.

Preface

It has been conventional to describe grazing management as an art rather than a science, despite a substantial input to grazing research over many years. This has been due in no small measure to the difficulties of achieving an understanding of the inter-relationships between plants and animals *under grazing conditions*, and the ways in which these interrelationships might influence output from grazing systems. Some progress in understanding has been achieved over the last 10–15 years, and in this book I have tried to bring together the available information and to relate it to the practical issues of planning and managing grazing systems.

I wish to record my thanks to a number of former colleagues (Dick Armstrong, Julio Arosteguy, Dick Baker, Titus Barthram, John Bircham, Jorge Combellas, Alison Davies, David Forbes, Sheila Grant, Stewart Jamieson, John King, Yann Le Du, Jeff Maxwell, John Milne, Jorge Rodriquez, Tim Treacher and Mike Wade) for permission to make extensive use of both published and unpublished information. The sources of other specific items of information are acknowledged in the text. Thanks are also due to Mrs Helen Tulloch, Mrs June Cave and Mrs Colette Gwynne for their patience in dealing with the preliminary drafts of the text, and to Mr Ian Pitkethly who provided most of the photographs and drew many of the figures for me.

Acknowledgements

We are indebted to the following for permission to reproduce copyright material:

The author, R. Anslow for figs. 11.1 & 11.2 (Anslow & Green, 1967); the author, Dr. W. Black for fig. 17.1 (Black, 1975); Blackwell Scientific Publications Ltd. for part of table 6.1 (1980); Blackwell Scientific Publications Ltd. and the respective authors for figs. 4.5 (Milne, Hodgson, Thomson, Souter & Barthram, 1982) & 6.2 (Terry & Tilley, 1964); C.A.B. International for part of table 6.1 (1980); Durrant Periodicals and the author, Dr. J. Milne for figs. 14.2 & 17.2 (Milne, Maxwell & Souter, 1981); the author, Dr. J. Frame for fig. 12.4 (Frame, 1975); the author, J. Green for figs. 6.4 & 11.3 (Green, Corrall & Terry, 1971); the Controller of Her Majesty's Stationery Office for part of table 6.1 (1975); the author, Prof. W. Holmes for fig. 14.3 (Holmes, 1975); the author, Dr. O. Jewiss for figs. 3.1a & 3.1b (Jewiss, 1981); Longman Group UK Ltd. for fig. 13.3 (Speedy, 1980); the author, P. Penning for fig. 7.4 (Penning 1985); the author, M. Robson for fig. 3.6 (Robson, 1973); the author, Dr. D. Wilman for fig. 6.3 (Wilman, Ojuederic & Asare, 1976).

Chapter 1

Grassland and grazing management

As a method of land utilization, grazing is of enormous importance on a world scale. Approximately 25 per cent of the total land area of the world is classified as grazing lands, and grazing animals also make substantial use of the cropping lands which occupy a further 10–15 per cent of the land area. In the UK, where many animals are housed during the winter, grassland and rough grazing meet 70–75 per cent of the nutrient requirements of the ruminant livestock population and about 70 per cent of the grassland contribution comes from grazing. In New Zealand, with a predominantly pastoral agriculture, around 90 per cent of the total nutrient requirements of ruminants come directly from grazing.

Ever since his earliest days as a hunter, man has made use of grazing animals as a means of gathering and concentrating nutrients from extensive areas of land which he would otherwise be unable to exploit. This is still the main function of grazing animals in many parts of the world, though increased standards of affluence in the developed countries have resulted in the development of livestock production enterprises which require land to be sown to pasture which otherwise could be used for the direct production of food crops. Whatever the long-term future of enterprises of this latter kind (bearing in mind that many of them also utilize crop by-products of no direct nutritional value for humans) there can be no doubt of the continuing importance of the basic function of the grazing animal as an exploiter of land resources which are best suited to the production of grass, and which would otherwise be of little use to man.

The output of animal products from a grassland enterprise is dependent first upon the basic resources of the farm – its soil and climate, and its populations of plants and animals; and next on major inputs like fertilizers, supplementary feeds, buildings and machinery. In this book attention is concentrated not so much on the resources themselves as on the ways in which the management of animals and pastures can influence the efficiency with which the basic resources are used. This is not in any sense to deny the importance of these resources, but readers should look elsewhere for detailed treatment of them. This book is concerned primarily with the management of grazing systems in temperate grassland areas. It relates principally to enclosed pastures, often with a substantial content of introduced plant species, and with a relatively high production potential.

The average level of output from grassland is normally only about half that achieved by the best grassland farmers, and their performance in turn is only about half that shown to be theoretically possible. This indicates the scope for improvement in production from grassland systems. The objective of management will not necessarily be an increase in output either per animal or per unit area of land, though it often is. Greater predictability or uniformity of production, or greater management convenience, may be more important objectives on many farms, and the ultimate practical test of any farming enterprise is its financial viability. However, appreciation of the scope for improvement and of the financial implications of any planned changes in management depends upon an understanding of the biological principles which determine plant and animal production.

Our understanding of the biology of grassland production owes much to the efforts of pioneers like Sir George Stapledon and Dr William Davies. However, despite the general importance of grazing as a method of land utilization, studies on the grazing process itself and the associations between grazed swards and grazing animals are a relatively recent development. Consequently, much of the detailed information used to develop ideas about grazing management has had to come from experiments on cut swards or housed animals. It is now known that evidence of this kind cannot always be applied with confidence to grazing conditions, and the arguments developed in this book rely as far as possible on evidence derived directly from grazing studies.

Chapter 2   The grazing system

The fundamental process in all conventional food production systems is the harnessing of the sun's energy and the supply of plant nutrients from the soil for the production of plant tissue. In systems of animal production there are two further stages: the plants must be consumed by animals, and then converted into usable animal products (Fig. 2.1). Each of these stages has its own efficiency (output expressed as a proportion of input) which can be

Figure 2.1   Stages of plant and animal production in grazing systems.

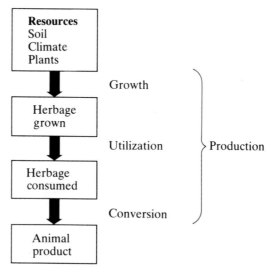

The grazing system is represented here as a simple series of three stages – herbage growth, consumption by grazing animals ('utilization'), and conversion into animal product. In fact the three stages interact with one another in a number of ways, the most important of which are shown in Fig. 2.2.

Figure 2.2   *Interactions between the stages of production in grazing systems.*

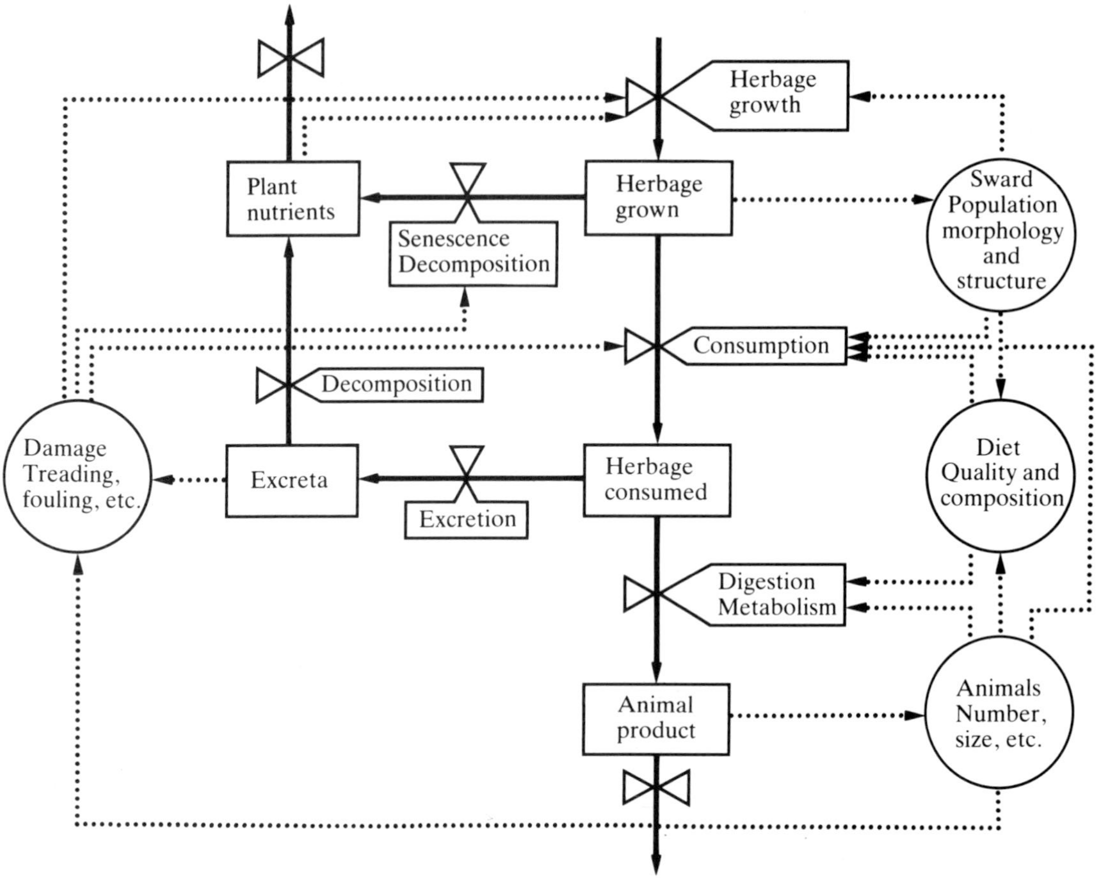

The central flow of nutrients is illustrated through the stages of herbage growth, utilization and conversion into animal product (see Fig. 2.1) and, in addition, some of the more important ways in which these stages interrelate are shown. There is a reverse flow of nutrients to the soil via excretion and decomposition. The main stages of production are linked through effects on the characteristics of the sward and of the diet consumed.

The boxes indicate quantities of material, solid lines indicate flows of material between boxes, and 'butterfly valves' indicate rates of flow. Circles and dashed lines indicate the factors involved in the relationships between the main stages of production and which interact to control the rates of flow. Only interactions between sward and animals are illustrated; other influences (of soil characteristics or climate on plant growth, for example) are not shown.

influenced by management, and together these efficiencies determine the production achieved.

In many enterprises the plant tissue (herbage) is harvested, and often stored, before it is fed to animals, so that the stages of crop growth and utilization are essentially independent of one another. In grazing systems, however, the stages cannot be separated in this way and the interactions between them exert an important influence on the eventual output of animal products. For example, the grazing animal may affect the rate of herbage growth (a) by removing plant material from the sward, (b) by direct physical damage to plants or soil, or (c) by recycling plant nutrients through excretion in faeces and urine. The grazing animal may itself be affected by the amount of herbage eaten and the nutritive value of the herbage. Some of the ways in which these interactions work are illustrated in Fig. 2.2.

As a consequence of the close interdependence between the stages of production, management decisions which improve efficiency at one stage may reduce it at another and vice versa. Examples will be given in later chapters. This limits the scope for increasing output by changing management, but it also limits the risk that a system will collapse as a consequence of wrong decisions. The essence of grassland management is to achieve an effective balance between the efficiencies of the three main stages of production: herbage growth, herbage consumption, animal production.

The grazed sward and the grazing animal will be considered separately, before going on to consider the interactions between them and the scope for controlling them to advantage. Throughout, the emphasis will be on the production and utilization of plant tissue, or plant energy, and little attention will be paid to the specific nutrient requirements of either plants or animals except where they impinge directly on aspects of grazing management. These are important issues, of course, but they have been dealt with in detail in other publications to which readers should refer for information. A list of references for further reading is given at the end of the book.

Chapter 3   The grazed sward

Function and structure

The primary functions of the plants in grazed swards, as of virtually all of the higher plants, are to trap sunlight in the foliage in order to ensure a supply of energy for growth, and to absorb water and mineral nutrients from the soil via the roots. The form and function of the plants are adapted to these ends, but are also strongly influenced by the strategies adopted to survive the consequences of defoliation and disturbance by grazing animals.

Typically, in successful grassland plants, the buds from which growth takes place are situated close to ground level where they are protected from direct damage. Further, the development of new plant tissue from these growth sites is a virtually continuous process so long as climatic conditions allow. These characteristics determine the typical growth form of temperate grasslands, which are principally populations of grasses, legumes and other broad-leaved herbaceous plants whose foliage forms a short, dense canopy.

Success in agricultural terms is also determined by vigour of growth. For these reasons the interest in plants for use in grazed swards has been concentrated on a limited number of grass and legume species. However, many other plants are normal constituents of grasslands, whether sown or indigenous, and can have important effects on the functioning of grazing systems.

The basic unit of production in the grasses is the tiller (Fig. 3.1). The tiller is essentially a single growing point encased in the sheaths of the leaves which grow from it, bearing its own root system, and having the capacity to develop new generations of tillers from buds at the bases of individual leaves. At germination each grass plant is in effect a single tiller, but development leads to the creation of a complex plant with many generations of tillers. Each new tiller rapidly develops roots and can then be regarded as largely self-supporting. However, the interconnections between 'parent' and 'daughter' tillers are not usually

Figure 3.1   *The grass tiller. (a) Illustration of an established plant of perennial ryegrass with four tillers; (b) stylized cross-section of a vegetative tiller. From Jewiss, O. R. (1981) In Hodgson, J. et al. (eds), Sward Measurement Handbook, British Grassland Society, pp. 93–114.*

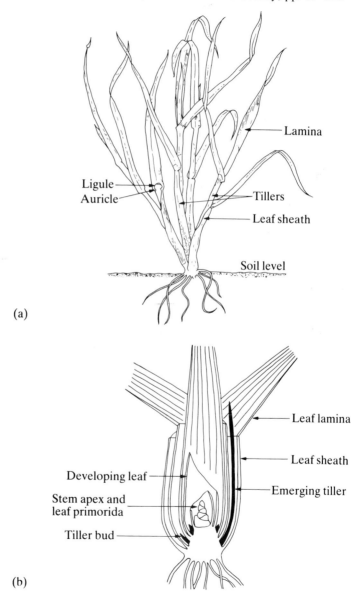

(a)

(b)

severed completely and can be important links for the transfer of nutrients following defoliation.

White clover (*Trifolium repens* L.) is the dominant legume in most grazed swards. Its growth depends upon the extension and repeated branching of a series of prostrate stems (or stolons) which grow along the soil surface from the crown of the original plant. Leaves, roots and buds with the potential for new branches arise at nodes which develop at intervals along the stolons (Fig. 3.2). The stolon branch is therefore the unit of growth most directly analogous to the grass tiller. This growth habit gives the white clover plant a mobility which the tillering grasses do not possess, and explains its success as a species for grazed grassland when compared with the other cultivated legumes which lack the stoloniferous habit and are much more sensitive to grazing. Some grasses (though none of importance in cultivated grasslands) have growth habits similar to white clover. Their horizontal stems may

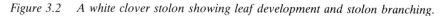

Figure 3.2   A white clover stolon showing leaf development and stolon branching.

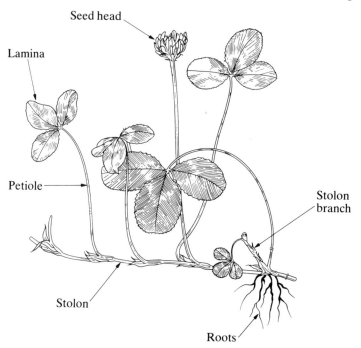

be on the soil surface (stolons) or beneath it (rhizomes), in either case making them vigorous colonizers. This contributes to the difficulties of controlling them if they are present as weeds in grassland or arable crops.

Because leaf growth takes place principally from the base of a sward, young leaves must penetrate the overlying vegetation before they can reach the light (Fig. 3.3). They eventually overtop older leaves so that a developing sward will steadily increase in height if it is not grazed. Older leaves senesce and die and, in consequence, the ratios of live to dead tissue, and of leaf to stem and sheath tissue, decline progressively from the top to the bottom of the sward canopy. Also, the density of plant material (weight per unit volume of space occupied) increases rapidly from the sward surface downwards so that a substantial proportion of the total amount of the herbage is concentrated close to the soil surface (Fig. 3.4 and Plate 3.1).

The morphology of the white clover plant means that a relatively high proportion of the total weight of tissue is held in the stolon, which is not normally removed by grazing animals. On the other hand, the proportion of the leaf tissue borne in the

Figure 3.3   *Cross-section of a mixed sward of grass and clover, illustrating the distribution of foliage within the sward canopy.*

Sward surface height

In simplified form, the distribution of leaf and stem material within the canopy of a mixed sward of grass and clover which is illustrated in Plate 3.1. Live leaf is concentrated in the upper layers of the sward, and stem and sheath material in the lower layers. Dead leaf works down to become concentrated close to the soil surface. The measurement of sward surface height, which is referred to frequently in later chapters, is also illustrated.

Figure 3.4   *(a) and (b) Diagrams of the density distribution of plant tissue within the sward canopy and the root zone.*

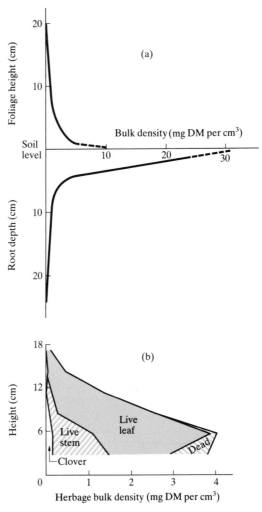

There is a high concentration of plant tissue close to the soil surface in all swards, both in the sward canopy and in the root zone (a). Within the canopy of a vegetative sward the leaf sheaths (which make up the 'stem' of the grass plant) and dead material are concentrated in the lower layers, and live leaf occurs principally in the upper layers (b). This is one way of showing in quantitative terms the vertical distribution of plant tissue which is illustrated in Fig. 3.3 and Plate 3.1.

upper regions of the sward, and therefore susceptible to defoliation, is greater in white clover than in the grasses (Fig. 3.5). These characteristics can have an important influence on the balance between grass and clover in mixed swards.

The sward-forming grasses and legumes create a mass of finely branched roots which are concentrated in the upper 10–20 cm of the soil, but individual roots may penetrate to a depth of 100–200 cm depending upon soil conditions and the depth of the water table. Roots invade the soil space by continuing extension growth and by branching continuously when temperature and water supply allow. Root density in the surface layers of the soil is usually much greater than herbage density in the sward canopy (Fig. 3.4(a)) but it is not easy to determine the relative proportions of functional and dead root tissue.

Plate 3.1   *A cross-section of grazed sward. The photograph illustrates the distribution of leaf, sheath and stem material in the sward canopy. Most of the tillers in the frame are perennial ryegrass (*Lolium perenne*) but the two seed heads in the centre are the common weed grass annual meadow grass (*Poa annua*). Note the high density of plant tissue in the middle and lower layers of the sward. The average distance from the ground surface to the tips of the upper leaves in this sward (sward surface height) was 3.5 cm. A diagrammatic representation of a similar sward is shown in Fig. 3.3.*

Figure 3.5   A diagram of the distribution of the foliage of grass and clover plants in the canopy of a mixed sward.

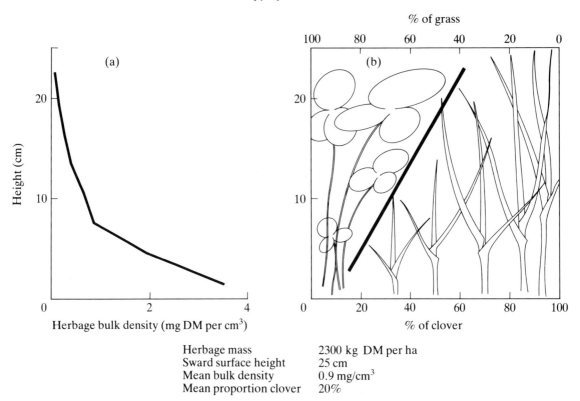

Herbage mass	2300 kg DM per ha
Sward surface height	25 cm
Mean bulk density	0.9 mg/cm^3
Mean proportion clover	20%

The general pattern of distribution of plant tissue within the canopy of this mixed sward of grass and clover (a) is similar to the distributions shown in Fig. 3.4. Clover stolons (not shown) are normally concentrated close to the ground surface, but the proportion of clover foliage increases progressively from the lower to the upper layers of the sward canopy (b). This is because clover leaves are usually arranged in a horizontal plane at the ends of slender petioles (Fig. 3.2) in contrast to the lanceolate leaves of grass plants, many of which are aligned at an angle close to vertical (Fig. 3.3). In this example the proportion of clover increases from less than 20 per cent in the bottom 5 cm of the sward to 40 per cent in the top 10 cm. This means that defoliation at any level within the sward canopy will have a more serious effect on the clover than on the grass component of the sward.

Plant growth

The production of new leaves on an individual grass tiller is a virtually continuous process. Each leaf has a characteristic growth cycle, a period of active extension growth leading to maturity and then to senescence and death whether or not the leaf has been grazed. Part of the extension growth takes place within the encircling tube of sheaths of older leaves before the tip of the extending leaf becomes visible, but by the time that a leaf blade is fully expanded it is likely to be between three and five times as long as the sheaths through which it grew. The life cycles of successive leaves on a tiller are closely linked, the appearance of a new leaf, the cessation of growth in the next oldest leaf and the senescence of a mature leaf occurring more or less in step (Fig. 3.6). This means that, in perennial ryegrass for example, each vegetative tiller characteristically has three visible live leaves at a time, only one of which will be actively growing.

The rate of leaf production and the rate of extension growth are strongly influenced by temperature. The interval between the appearance of successive leaves on a tiller can vary from less than a week in summer to a month in winter, and the life span of individual leaves from appearance to senescence varies from approximately 1 month in summer to 2 months or more in winter. The ultimate size of a leaf is closely related to the size of the tiller on which it grows, which in turn reflects the stage of development of the tiller and sward management.

The production of new tillers, on the other hand, is usually an intermittent process which may be triggered off by the defoliation of the plant and the consequent improvement in illumination at the base of the sward. Individual tillers have a limited life span, which may be up to a year but is frequently only a matter of weeks. Thus, the population of tillers can only be maintained by continuous replacement. This can be achieved almost indefinitely in most temperate, sward-forming grass species by appropriate management and is the basis of grass perenniality; successive generations of vegetative tillers maintain production from one year to the next.

The above description refers to tillers in a vegetative phase of growth. In the spring, however, many of the tillers overwintering from the previous year switch from vegetative to reproductive growth, leading to the development of a flowering stem and seed head and the production and setting of seed. High rates of herbage production are associated with this phase of growth, because

Figure 3.6 *The time sequence of the phases of extension and maturity in successive leaves on a tiller. From Robson, M. J. (1973) Annals of Botany, 37, 487–500.*

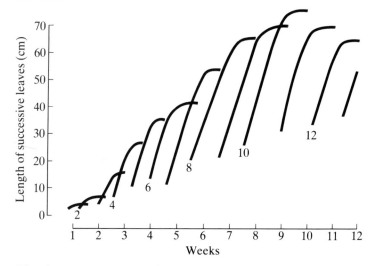

The characteristic pattern of growth in successive leaves on a growing tiller kept in a constant environment is illustrated. The first two leaves are seedling leaves. Each growth curve starts when a leaf is first observed as it emerges from the sheath of the preceding leaf (see Fig. 3.1), but in fact the linear phase of growth starts when the leaf is extending within the sheath and continues after it emerges. The rate of extension decelerates quickly as the leaf approaches maturity and the ligule emerges from the sheath of the previous leaf. Comparison of successive growth curves will show a close coincidence between the first appearance of one leaf and the rapid deceleration of growth in the preceding leaf. The progressive increase in the final length of successive leaves reflects the increasing size of an undefoliated tiller.

Leaf elongation rate is strongly influenced by temperature, so in normal conditions, with fluctuating environmental temperatures, the patterns of leaf extension would be much less uniform than shown here.

of the weight of plant tissue accumulating in the extending stem and expanding seed head. Other important changes in the physiology of the tiller occur at the same time. The development of new leaves ceases once stem elongation commences, so that leaf production from that tiller will cease when the existing leaves are fully extended, and the development of any young tillers is blocked until the reproductive stem is cut off or dies.

The population of tillers in an intermittently defoliated sward usually increases to a peak in the spring, declines rapidly over the flowering season, and then remains roughly constant until the following spring (Fig. 3.7). In contrast, tiller populations in continuously stocked swards are relatively stable, and remain at a higher level throughout.

The patterns of leaf and stolon development and loss in white clover are similar to those described for grass leaves and tillers. There are usually three to six live leaves per stolon at any time, but continued leaf production depends upon the continuation of

Figure 3.7   *The annual cycle of tiller population density in a grass sward cut at monthly intervals.*

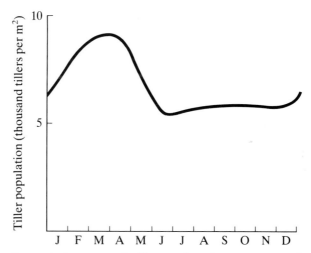

In regularly cut swards tiller numbers increase to a maximum in early spring with the appearance of large numbers of small tillers, fall steeply during the period of reproductive growth when competition for light and nutrients is fierce, and are relatively stable through the summer and autumn. However, the pattern of change in the tiller population can be markedly affected by management. For instance, delayed cutting during reproductive development can result in a substantially greater loss of tillers, whereas seasonal fluctuations are likely to be much smaller under continuous stocking management (see Fig. 3.10). The number of tillers per unit area (expressed here in thousands per square metre) is also very sensitive to management (see Ch. 5).

stolon development. The production of flower heads occurs later in the year in clover than in the grasses, and is normally spread over a longer period in time, so the seasonal cycles of herbage production in the grasses and clover are very different (Ch. 5).

Senescence and decomposition

The processes which determine the links between the appearance of a new leaf and senescent changes in the oldest living leaf on a tiller are not well understood but, once started, the degenerative changes are rapid and inexorable. The visible signs are of progressive yellowing and eventually browning and dehydration. In the early stages of senescence some of the soluble components may be remobilized for use elsewhere in the plant, but most of the cell contents are used up in respiration by the leaf itself or by bacteria and fungi living on plant tissue, or lost to leaching. The leaf is likely to lose up to 50 per cent of its original mature weight over this phase (Fig. 3.8). The dried leaf skeleton even-

Figure 3.8   *The sequence of change in the dry weights of successive leaves on a grass tiller.*

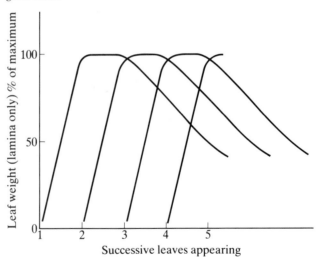

Changes in leaf length and leaf weight parallel one another to maturity (compare Figs 3.6 and 3.8). Then, following a short period of stability, the leaf blades start to lose weight with the onset of the processes of senescence and decay. By the time a leaf is dry and dead it will have lost approximately half its mature weight.

tually becomes detached and works its way down to the litter layer before ultimately becoming incorporated into the soil, or it may be taken down below the soil surface by earthworms. The final digestion and decomposition of leaf skeleton is the function of soil- and litter-living bacteria and fungi.

Dead tillers pass through the same degenerative changes as leaves though, because of their greater bulk, the changes may be slower. Old seed heads and stems with extensive lignification decay very slowly, and may remain in the sward for many weeks. The processes of decomposition work fastest in warm, damp conditions, and can be greatly inhibited in the absence of moisture. Thus a build-up of dead plant material is frequently observed in dry summer conditions as dead seeding tillers accumulate, but this material disappears with a return to moist conditions in autumn.

Plant competition and sward flexibility

So far swards have been considered as collections of relatively uniform tillers or stolon nodes, each with its own essentially independent existence. This is far from the case. Any sward contains a population of individual tillers of different size and at different stages of development, and even the simplest sown sward is likely to contain a substantial proportion of volunteer plants in addition to the cultivars which were sown. For most of the life of a sward these plants will be in competition with one another for light, mineral nutrients and water, and for the foliage and root spaces which allow access to these resources.

The influence of competition is most apparent in mixed plant communities where marked changes in the relative proportions of different species can occur in response to minor changes in management, or simply as a consequence of natural successional changes without interference by man. The success of the representatives of a particular species in mixed swards depends upon the speed with which they can colonize bare areas of soil, the aggressiveness with which they occupy space once established, and their tolerance of the existing environmental limitations and of effects of defoliation or other disturbance. In this sense sward management may be considered as a means of achieving and maintaining a desired balance of plant species in a sward, and this aspect of management will be considered later. The most important applications of sward management relate to attempts to retain sown species in a new sward, to control the balance between grass and clover in a mixed sward, and to manipulate the species balance in indigenous plant communities.

The control of competition between individual plants or tillers of the *same* species can also be an important management tool. The initiation of development growth in quiescent tiller buds is dependent upon the stimulus of defoliation and light penetration at the base of the sward. Once a tiller is established its survival rapidly becomes dependent upon access to light for the generation of new plant tissue. Both the initiation and maintenance of tiller growth are influenced by the support of the parent tiller and by competition from the surrounding tillers which are themselves likely to be at different stages of establishment. In most circumstances survival is lowest in small tillers and greatest in large, well-established tillers.

Because of these competitive effects and the capacity for continuous production of new leaves and tillers or stolons, the morphology and structure of a sward can change rapidly in response to a change in management. There is normally a close functional relationship between tiller population density (number per unit area) and the size of individual tillers in a sward, tiller size decreasing progressively as tiller population density increases (Fig. 3.9). This is true in a sward allowed to regrow after cutting

Figure 3.9   The relationship between tiller population density and the weight of individual tillers in the population.

For any given environment there is a negative relationship between the tiller population and the weight of individual tillers. Managements which result in an increase in tiller size and weight will reduce tiller population, and vice versa. In practice continual adjustments in tiller number and size are likely in response to sward changes and climatic fluctuations.

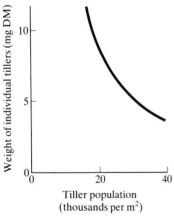

or grazing in which, after an initial increase in response to the defoliation stimulus, tiller numbers tend to decline and individual tillers increase in size. It is also true under continuous stocking, where close grazing treatments reduce tiller size and at the same time provide a greater stimulus to tillering than does lax grazing. Also, close grazing reduces the risk of tiller mortality as a consequence of competition for light. The result is that tiller populations can vary from 10 000 tillers per square metre under lax grazing to as high as 60 000 tillers per square metre on closely grazed swards. However, grazing can become so severe that the

Figure 3.10 *Tiller populations in intermittently grazed and continuously stocked swards.*

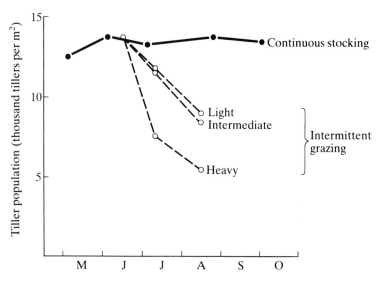

Intermittently grazed swards usually have lower tiller populations than continuously stocked swards grazed at similar efficiencies because the tiller population tends to adjust to tiller size at the end of a phase of growth rather than that immediately after grazing. Heavy intermittent grazing can result in the death of substantial numbers of tillers, so depressing the tiller population.

These results refer to perennial ryegrass swards in southern England grazed by dairy cows. The tiller populations shown here and in Fig. 3.7 are substantially lower than the populations observed under continuous stocking with sheep (Ch. 5).

tiller population is reduced, as a consequence of high losses, with no compensatory increase in tiller size. This will inevitably have serious effects upon herbage production. Intermittently grazed swards usually have substantially smaller populations of large tillers than continuously stocked swards at similar stocking rates (Fig. 3.10).

Energy: photosynthesis and respiration

Plant growth is fuelled by the energy in simple sugars which are produced in the process of photosynthesis when the chlorophyll in green leaf tissue is exposed to sunlight. This process traps light energy in a form useful to the plant by combining carbon dioxide from the air with water from the soil to form simple carbohydrates (Fig. 3.11). Plant tissue itself is made up largely of more complex carbohydrates synthesized from these simple products. Thus photosynthesis is vital to the life of plants and to the maintenance of life on earth. Energy production in a sward is a relatively inefficient process for all that, only between 2 and 5 per cent of the light energy reaching the sward surface from the sun being converted into useful energy for plant growth. The determinants of energy accumulation in a sward are (a) the effectiveness with which light is intercepted by the leaf canopy, and (b) the efficiency of the photosynthetic process itself.

Light interception is a function of the amount of leaf in a sward which, for this purpose, is expressed as the leaf area index or LAI. The LAI is defined as the surface area of leaf lamina (measured on one side only) per unit area of ground. The LAI at which virtually all of the incident light is intercepted (the criti-

Figure 3.11   Photosynthesis.

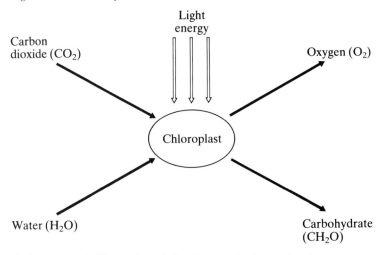

A diagrammatic illustration of the photosynthetic reaction in chloroplasts in the cells of green plant tissue. Photosynthesis is most active in the leaves, but there is also some activity in other green tissues. Carbon dioxide enters the leaves from the surrounding air through stomata in the leaf surface, and passes into the cells by diffusion. Water is transported to the leaves from the roots.

cal leaf area) is usually in the range from 4 to 6 for grass and grass/clover swards (Fig. 3.12). However, the critical LAI varies with the angle of incidence of sunlight and with the structure of the sward canopy, being lower when the sun is low in the sky in winter, and lower in swards where the leaves are arranged horizontally than in swards with more erect leaves. Thus clover, for example, has a lower critical leaf area than most grasses.

The efficiency of the photosynthetic process (the proportion of light energy converted into plant energy) is inversely related to the intensity of light falling on the leaf surface and declines to a low level at the high light intensities experienced during the summer months. However, in absolute terms the amount of carbon

Figure 3.12   The relationship between LAI and light interception by a grass sward.

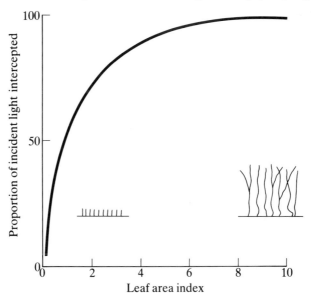

The proportion of the light falling on the surface of the sward which is intercepted by leaf tissue before it reaches the ground increases progressively as the leaf area per unit of ground area (LAI) increases. In normal conditions light interception is close to 100 per cent at an LAI of between 4 and 6. However, when the sun is low, or in a sward with a high proportion of plants like clover whose leaves are held close to the horizontal, complete light interception will be achieved at a lower LAI.

fixed increases with increasing light intensity. Scattering of light within the canopy improves the photosynthetic efficiency of the sward by reducing the intensity of light incident on any individual leaf surface. This means that at any given LAl the yield of photosynthate is likely to be greater, other things being equal, in a tall sward with erect leaves where light scatter is substantial than in a short sward with prostrate leaves where scatter is limited.

The structure and morphology of the sward can have other effects on photosynthetic efficiency, however. Young leaves have a higher efficiency than older leaves, and grass leaves developed in high light intensity have a higher efficiency than those grown in the shade. In contrast, the efficiency of clover leaves is not affected by shading during development. Thus there is some conflict of interest between (a) the need to maintain a sward with a high enough LAl to ensure effective interception and scattering of incoming sunlight, and (b) the need to maintain the photosynthetic efficiency of individual leaves by ensuring that young leaves are exposed as soon as possible to direct sunlight and are not shaded by older leaves or senescent, non-productive tissue.

The carbohydrate produced in photosynthesis is used in part for the synthesis of cell contents and structural tissues, but up to 50 per cent of it is used as a source of energy to support the growth of new tissue in leaves, stems and roots and to maintain the life processes in established tissue. These energy demands result in the loss of carbon dioxide to the atmosphere in respiration. Respiration losses account for a substantial proportion of the carbon assimilated in photosynthesis, the proportion increasing with increasing LAl as the weight of plant tissue to be maintained increases. Degenerative changes in senescing plant tissue and the activities of decomposer organisms also make substantial contributions to respiratory losses.

The result of these effects is that as a sward is allowed to grow after defoliation, the *net* rate of carbon assimilation (the difference between photosynthetic gain and respiratory loss) increases with increasing LAl to a maximum, and declines with further increase in LAl (Fig. 3.13). Net carbon assimilation would eventually decline to zero in an undefoliated grass crop, though this is clearly of no interest to the grassland manager. This evidence has formed an important component of advice on cutting and grazing management, and procedures designed to hold

Figure 3.13   *The relationships between LAI, the rates of carbon assimilation in photosynthesis and loss in respiration, and the net carbon balance during regrowth in a cut sward.*

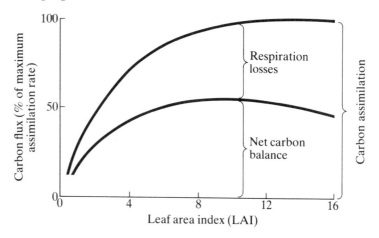

Increasing LAI results in an increase in light interception (Fig. 3.12) and, often, an improvement in the efficiency of photosynthesis because of the greater degree of scatter of light within the sward canopy. Thus, the rate of carbon assimilation per unit area of ground increases with increasing LAI as a sward grows, and eventually reaches a plateau level at high LAI. However, respiration losses increase in proportion to the increasing mass of herbage with the result that the net carbon balance (= assimilation − respiration) reaches a maximum at intermediate LAI and then declines.

swards close to the LAI maximizing net carbon assimilation, or at least allowing LA1 to fluctuate on either side of the optimum, have been strongly advocated. However, the decline in the rate of net carbon assimilation at low LAl is not so serious on continuously stocked or very frequently cut swards as it is on swards cut or grazed at longer intervals. This is because tiller populations are maintained at high levels on swards which are kept short, resulting in large numbers of young leaves which, because they have developed in bright light, have a high photosynthetic potential. Also, the increasingly prostrate growth habit of leaves on these swards means that light interception is more effective than at equivalent levels of LAl on intermittently defoliated swards. The effects of sward management upon herbage production and utilization are considered in detail in Chapter 5.

Carbohydrates surplus to the immediate requirements for tissue maintenance and growth are retained in the plant as reserves which can be called upon later if the demand for assimilation exceeds supply, as it may do, for instance, following severe defoliation when most of the leaf tissue is removed. Most grasses retain some reserve carbohydrate at the base of the stem, and in white clover the stolon is an important storage organ.

Plant nutrients

The maintenance of growth in pasture plants, as in all other plants, is dependent upon the supply of mineral nutrients, the most important of which are nitrogen (N), phosphorus (P) and potassium (K). These nutrients may be made available to the plant by release from soil particles as a consequence of breakdown by physical and biochemical agencies, by mineralization of plant or animal residues during decomposition, and by the addition of fertilizers to the soil. Clover and other legumes make a direct contribution to the N economy of a sward because the symbiotic bacteria (*Rhizobium* spp.) growing in nodules on the plant roots are capable of fixing N directly from the atmosphere. Plant nutrients are discussed in more detail in Chapter 12.

Chapter 4   The grazing animal

The success of herbivorous animals in evolutionary terms, and eventually their value as farm animals, depended upon their ability to derive an adequate intake of nutrients from a food resource which was often fibrous in nature and of low nutrient concentration, and which, because of the structure of the sward canopy (as already seen in Fig. 3.3), could be difficult to harvest. There were two important adaptations which made effective harvesting of grass possible: first, the modifications of the jaws and teeth which improved the efficiency of the harvesting process, and, secondly, the development of a digestive system in which symbiotic cellulolytic bacteria were responsible for breaking down by fermentation the refractory plant fibre and cell walls which would otherwise be largely unaffected by normal mammalian digestion. The latter process was aided by the development of an enlarged section of the alimentary tract in which food could be held for fermentation. In the case of ruminants like cattle and sheep this enlarged section (the rumen) occurs at the beginning of the digestive tract; in the case of the horse and rabbit it occurs towards the end of the tract (the caecum).

Modern farming methods have done much to improve the nutritive value of herbage throughout the year, but the main function of the herbivores is still to deal with large amounts of food of lower nutrient concentration than the diets offered to animals like pigs and poultry which have simple digestive tracts, and whose diets are based on seeds and seed products which are highly concentrated sources of nutrients. For example, in the course of a day a cow weighing 500 kg is likely to eat up to one-quarter of her own live weight of fresh herbage, equivalent to 12–16 kg of herbage dry matter (DM) occupying the volume of a 1 m cube and dispersed over a ground area of 100–500 m².

Digition The basis of ruminant digestion is the development of a complex stomach, the first two sections of which, the **rumen** and **reticulum**, together form a large sac in which food can be held for many hours (Fig. 4.1). This allows time for the complex carbohydrates of plant cell walls and support tissues to be broken down by bacterial fermentation. Some of the liquid and gaseous products of fermentation are absorbed through the rumen wall, together with the water which may be ingested in large volumes with grazed herbage. Many of the fermentation products, however, are incorporated into the tissues of the bacteria and must then be digested lower down the alimentary tract. The act of rumination – the regurgitation and remastication of partly digested food from the rumen – aids this process by reducing food particles to a smaller size.

The third stomach, or **omasum**, acts as a sieve to retain large particles of food, and also absorbs water from the digest passing through it. The bacterial cells are digested in the fourth or true stomach, the **abomasum**, and in the small intestine (Fig. 4.1). The products of digestion, and any soluble constituents of the diet or products of rumen fermentation which have not been incorporated into bacterial tissue, are absorbed into the bloodstream from the small intestine.

The digestibility of the diet – the proportion of the food consumed which disappears in passage through the alimentary tract – is used as a measure of the efficiency of the digestive process and frequently as an expression of the nutritive value of the diet. The digestibility of plant tissue can range from between 80 and 90 per cent in immature leaves and sheaths down to between 40 and 50 per cent in mature flowering stems, and to even lower levels in woody tissue (Ch. 6). In contrast, ripe seeds like cereals, and storage roots or tubers, consistently have a digestibility to ruminants of 75–85 per cent.

In the early stages of life, during which they are entirely reliant upon milk, calves and lambs function as monogastric animals. The initial digestion of milk takes place in the abomasum, and the first three stomachs are undeveloped. These stomachs develop very rapidly in size and function once the young animal starts to eat solid food, which it will do at about 3 weeks of age in lambs and calves. Full digestive efficiency is reached quickly in normal circumstances because the young animal acquires the typical spectrum of rumen micro-organisms from the adult

Figure 4.1   The ruminant digestive tract.

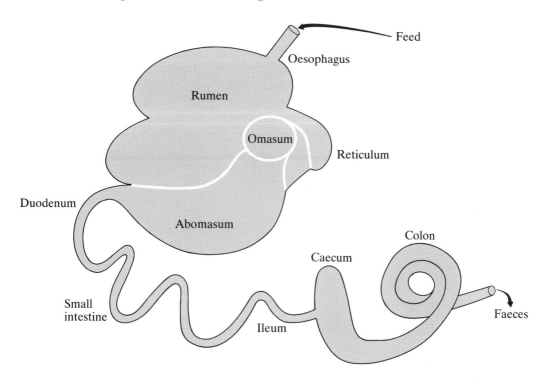

Food passes first into the rumen and reticulum, where it is held for several hours for microbial fermentation. Enzymic digestion starts in the abomasum or true stomach, and continues in the small intestine. Nutrients are absorbed from the small intestine into the bloodstream. Water is also absorbed from the residues of digestion in the caecum and colon, and some limited fermentation occurs before the residues are expelled as faeces.

   The extent or efficiency of digestion is measured in terms of the proportion of the feed eaten which disappears in passage through the alimentary tract. Conventionally:

Apparent digestibility (%) $= \dfrac{Feed - Faeces}{Feed} \times 100$

This calculation is influenced by the presence in the faeces of some residues from the body of the animal in addition to feed residues, which explains the use of the term 'apparent digestibility'.

animals with which it comes in contact, and the capacity of the alimentary tract reaches normal adult proportions, relative to body-weight, by about 12 and 16 weeks of age in lambs and calves respectively.

Jaws and teeth   In all ruminant animals the skull is elongated and bluntly pointed, facilitating penetration of the nose and head into vegetation. The pointed shape is more extreme in sheep than in cattle. In sheep, too, the mobile lips help in gathering vegetation into the mouth, whereas in cattle this function is served by the long, prehensile tongue and the lips are fleshier and less mobile. The mouth parts of the two species are similar (Fig. 4.2). In place of the upper incisor teeth there is a thick pad of connective tissue against which the chisel-like lower incisors close to grip each mouthful of herbage before it is severed by a quick jerk of the head. The molars, the main grinding teeth, are heavily ridged, and the lower jaw is articulated to allow side-to-side movement which increases the effectiveness of the grinding process. The large gap between the incisors and the molars (which, in most other animals, is occupied by the canine teeth) provides room for tongue movements

Figure 4.2   The jaws and teeth of the cow.

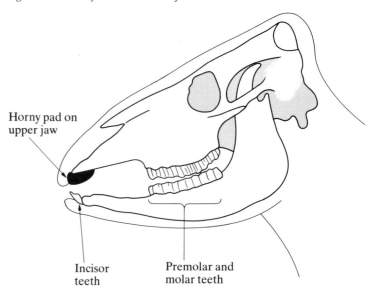

Horny pad on
upper jaw

Incisor
teeth

Premolar and
molar teeth

associated with the collection and manipulation of plant leaves and stems.

Both incisor and molar teeth are subject to heavy wear because of the fibrous and abrasive nature of much plant material and its frequent contamination with soil. The young ruminant is born with a set of incisor and premolar teeth, and these juvenile (milk) teeth are replaced by a full set of adult teeth by 3–4 years of age in both sheep and cattle.

Grazing behaviour Despite these adaptive changes the food-gathering process is still a demanding one for grazing animals (Plate 4.1). A cow has a

Plate 4.1 The grazing process.

mowing machine only 8–9 cm wide (the distance across the incisor teeth) and even though she uses her tongue to increase the effective area grazed, the weight of herbage obtained at a single bite is likely to be only 0.2–1.0 g of herbage DM in most circumstances. Thus, in order to achieve a daily herbage DM intake of 12–16 g she will have to take between 20 000 and 40 000 individual bites over periods of grazing activity occupying, in total, between 6 and 12 hours, depending upon sward conditions. In that time she will have walked 3–4 km. Sheep have smaller appetites and smaller mouths in absolute terms, though not relative to body size, but their total grazing effort, measured in terms of the number of grazing bites and the distance travelled, is similar. In addition to the work involved in grazing, ruminating activity is likely to occupy between 6 and 8 hours daily, and a further 15 000–20 000 jaw movements.

Animals given cut herbage or conserved forage indoors spend much less time eating, usually only 4–6 hours daily, though the extent of ruminating activity is similar to that under grazing conditions. The total energy expenditure of grazing animals, involves the effort of searching for and eating food, and meeting the demands exerted by exposure to the normal range of climatic conditions. However, in most circumstances this expenditure is probably only 10–20 per cent higher than that of comparable animals indoors.

Cattle and sheep normally divide their working day into alternating periods of grazing, rumination and rest. There are usually between three and five periods of grazing during the day, the longest and most intensive being after dawn and before dusk (Fig. 4.3). Most grazing activity occurs during daylight hours in temperate climates, though short periods of night grazing are not uncommon. There is usually a period of ruminating activity after each grazing period, but much of the rumination occurs at night. This characteristic pattern can be affected by routine activities like milking or moving animals to fresh pasture and, exceptionally, by extreme weather conditions, but in most circumstances it is very stable and all the members of a flock or herd tend to follow the same pattern.

Grazing activity may be temporarily suspended during heavy rain, particularly in cold or windy conditions, but the effects are transitory and daily grazing times do not seem to be particularly sensitive to climatic variations.

Figure 4.3   The diurnal pattern of grazing and ruminating activity in cattle.

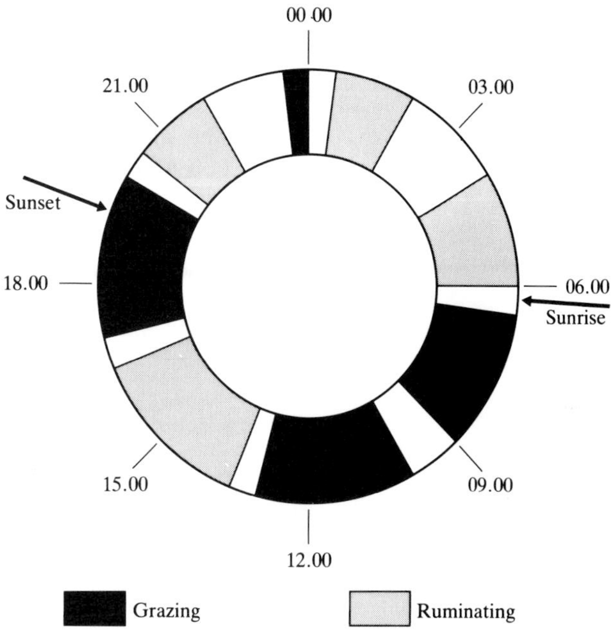

The pattern of grazing and ruminating activity of a member of a group of weaned calves 12–14 weeks old, during one day in autumn, is illustrated. There were three main periods of grazing during the day–one starting at dawn, the second occurring during the late morning, and a third in the evening ceasing at dusk. A fourth, limited period of grazing activity occurred around midnight. Most of the ruminating activity occurred during the hours of darkness when the calf was resting, but there was also a period of rumination during the afternoon. The blank sections include periods of standing or lying without either grazing or ruminating activity, and include time spent drinking, moving about or simply resting.

  With minor variations due to the effects of day length, weather and management this is a typical example of the activity patterns of both cattle and sheep. In this case the renewed grazing activity at 10.00 was stimulated by a move to a new area of pasture. Most of the members of a group of animals normally graze at the same time, but there is more variation between individuals in the pattern of ruminating activity. In this case the average time spent grazing by members of the group was 8.6 hours, and the average ruminating time was 7.8 hours per day.

When grazing intensively, a cow or a sheep will walk forward with its head held low and swinging from side to side in order to prospect a strip of sward 1–2 m wide, biting off mouthfuls of herbage at the rate of between one and two bites per second. The direction of travel is erratic but the collection and ingestion of herbage are almost continuous. This pattern of behaviour is typical of the main grazing periods on uniform, leafy swards. On more heterogeneous swards or towards the end of a grazing period even on highly nutritious swards, animals tend to move faster, to hold their heads higher, and to snatch single bites or groups of bites in passing. The rate of biting will be much slower, probably no more than thirty to forty bites per minute. In some

Figure 4.4   The development of grazing and ruminating activity in young calves.

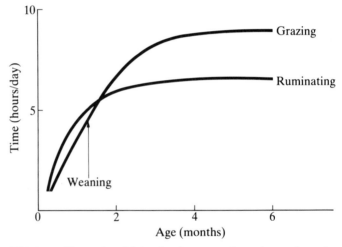

This is an illustration of the development of grazing and ruminating activity in artificially reared calves which were given limited quantities of milk to encourage early herbage intake and weaned at 1 month old. Grazing activity develops more slowly in calves receiving larger quantities of milk, whether by artificial means or by natural suckling, but in all cases increases rapidly to adult levels after the animal is weaned. Ruminating activity reflects the amount of herbage eaten, and so shows a similar pattern of development; it is also influenced by the digestibility of the diet, the time spent ruminating per kilogram of herbage eaten declining as the digestibility of the herbage increases.

The patterns of development in grazing and ruminating activity in lambs are similar.

cases they may walk purposefully from one patch of herbage to another, but in other cases they appear to take intermittent mouthfuls of herbage in the course of an essentially random pattern of movement.

Young ruminants start to nibble herbage in a seemingly indiscriminate manner when they are only a few days old. Serious grazing is likely to start by 3 weeks of age in lambs and calves and subsequently the duration and pattern of grazing and ruminating activity develop rapidly to adult standards (Fig. 4.4).

Selective grazing

The diet eaten by grazing animals usually contains higher proportions of leaf and live plant tissue in general, and lower proportions of stem and dead tissue, than are found in the sward as a whole. This means that the nutritive value of the diet is usually higher that that of the whole sward. Also, animals grazing a mixed sward frequently tend to graze some plant species and avoid others. These well-recognized patterns of behaviour are usually interpreted, with good reason, as indications of the deliberate exercise of choice by the grazing animal. However, the

Figure 4.5 The relationship between the clover content of the diet of grazing sheep and of the surface horizons of the sward. From Milne, J. A., Hodgson, J., Thomson, R., Souter, W. G. and Barthram, G. T. (1982) Grass and Forage Science, 37, 209–18.

In this example, taken from a series of young vegetative swards, there was close agreement between the clover content of the herbage eaten by grazing sheep and the clover content of the surface layers of the sward, indicating non-selective grazing within these surface layers. The line shown indicates equality between sward and diet. In more mature swards, with a greater contrast between the individual components, there may often be more evidence that animals are deliberately exercising choice (Table 4.1).

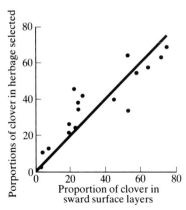

factors which determine selection are not well understood, and care is needed in making assumptions about its importance, particularly under intensive grazing management. For example, animals will often graze apparently indiscriminately in the surface layers of a sown sward, so that the botanical composition of the herbage consumed is very similar to the composition of the surface horizons (Fig. 4.5). In these circumstances any difference between the composition of the diet and that of the sward as a whole will reflect the non-uniform distribution of different components within the sward canopy, rather than any deliberate exercise of choice by the animal.

It is helpful to distinguish between (a) **preference**, the discrimination which would be exhibited between the components of a sward if all were available without restriction; and (b) **selection**, which is a measure of the choice demonstrated in practice. The composition of the diet selected reflects preference modified by the inevitable limitations to the opportunity for selection which occur in the field. Preference is principally a reflection of the animals' response to the chemical and physical characteristics of the leaves and stems of particular plant species as they affect the senses of sight, touch, taste and smell. Taste and smell are probably the most important in determining ultimate choice between the components of a sward, but sight and touch influence the initial approach to, and appraisal of, the components.

The taste and smell receptors in the epithelial lining of the tongue and the nasal passages are only sensitive to relatively simple volatile or soluble chemical entities. Thus, preference is unlikely to be influenced directly by the complex groupings of chemical compounds measured in the normal analyses of the nutrient content of plants and swards. The surface characteristics of plants have a direct effect on the touch receptors on the muzzle, lips and tongue, and hence on preference. Thus coarse, spiny and hairy plants or plant parts tend to be avoided, but it is not always succulent or smooth plants that are preferred. The opportunity for selection is influenced by the relative proportions of the different plant species and morphological components, and their distribution relative to one another in the sward canopy. The chance of a preferred component being selectively grazed will be less if it is distributed close to the base of a sward, or intimately mixed with other components, than if it grows close to the sward surface or in discrete clumps.

Preference as defined above can only be measured in very closely controlled conditions. Selection is easier to measure, and is usually expressed as a selection index, the proportion of a component in the diet expressed as a fraction of the proportion of the same component in the sward; index values higher than 1.0 indicate positive selection, values less than 1.0 indicate avoidance.

Preference and selection are both purely relative terms, and the intensity of selection for a particular component in the sward depends on the other components which are present and the contrasts which exist between them. For example, the intensity of selection by sheep for white clover in an indigenous *Agrostis*–

*Table 4.1 An example of the way in which the composition of the sward influences selective grazing**

Sward	No. of observations	Clover selection index	
		Mean	Range
(a) Sown: ryegrass/clover	9	1.1	0.6–2.0
(b) Indigenous: mixed	5	3.1	1.3–8.0

* This example illustrates the contrast between the degree of selection for white clover observed in (a) simple sown swards of perennial ryegrass and white clover which were well grazed throughout the year, and (b) indigenous swards containing 10–12 grass species (predominantly *Agrostis* and *Festuca*) and 8–10 herbs, and which included much mature herbage as a result of underutilization. Selection for clover is measured in terms of the selection index, which is calculated as

$$\text{Selection index} = \frac{\text{\% of clover in the herbage eaten}}{\text{\% of clover in the sward}}$$

The risks of assuming that a high index (where a value of 1.0 indicates neutrality) demonstrates deliberate selection by the animal are discussed in the text. There was little evidence of consistent discrimination between the grass and clover components of the sown sward, but in the indigenous sward the proportion of clover in the diet was substantially higher than that in the sward. In the latter case evidence for deliberate selection was reinforced by the fact that much of the clover lay close to the base of the sward and would therefore have to be searched for by the sheep.

Festuca sward is substantially greater than that for the same species in an intensively managed perennial ryegrass/white clover sward (Table 4.1). The degree of discrimination, and even the order of preference for particular species or plant parts, may also vary between individual animals and may change with time. Thus, though it is possible to recognize some characteristic patterns in selective grazing behaviour, great care is needed in attempting to explain these patterns and to generalize from them.

Sheep tend to be more selective grazers than cattle in most circumstances. Goats tend to avoid clover, and show a greater preference for fibrous plants than do sheep and cattle.

It is often suggested that young animals are more selective grazers than adults. There is no very conclusive evidence that this is so under comparable sward conditions, and in many circumstances young and mature animals grazing together select similar diets (Fig. 4.6). However, patterns of diet selection may be more unstable in young than in adult animals.

Figure 4.6   *A comparison of the digestibility of the herbage selected by dairy cows and weaned calves from three perennial ryegrass swards.*

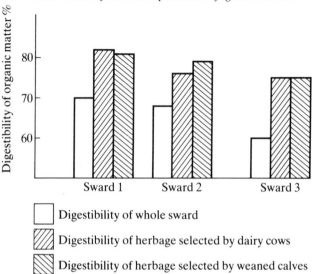

Digestibility of whole sward

Digestibility of herbage selected by dairy cows

Digestibility of herbage selected by weaned calves

In this trial, dairy cows were compared with weaned calves which had considerable grazing experience. The digestibility (see Ch. 6) of the herbage eaten by cows and calves was very similar, indicating a similar degree of diet selection. However, differences may be more apparent where cows are compared with younger calves, indicating a greater degree of instability in the grazing activities of inexperienced animals.

A comparison between the diets of cattle and sheep is shown in Fig. 7.6.

Note that although both cows and calves were consuming herbage with a digestibility 10–15 percentage units higher than that of the sward as a whole, this does not necessarily imply that they were exercising a preference for the most digestible material. Where herbage digestibility declines progressively from the surface to the base of a sward (see Ch. 6), animals grazing at the sward surface would automatically eat herbage of higher than average digestibility even if they exercised no choice at all.

Other effects on the sward

Grazing animals defecate and urinate at intervals as they move about, though substantial quantities of dung and urine tend to be deposited in the vicinity of areas which the animals choose to use as night camps or for daytime shade. This results in uneven distribution of the plant nutrients in excreta and uneven grazing because animals, particularly cattle, tend to avoid grazing close to dung pats. Conversely, grazing may be concentrated in the vicinity of urine patches, particularly during the drier months. Uneven grazing may also occur as a result of the patchy distribution of different plant species in a sward.

The activities of grazing animals can result in direct sward damage. These effects range from physical damage to soil and sward as a result of hoof pressure, particularly in wet conditions, through the smothering effect of dung and the scorching which can result from high concentrations of urine, to the uprooting of tillers or patches of sward as a result of the plucking action of grazing. All of these factors can influence herbage production and utilization.

Chapter 5   Herbage production and utilization

Patterns of defoliation

When animals are confined to a limited area and graze the sward down over a short period of time it is seldom that individual leaves or tillers are completely defoliated at a single bite. Rather, the sward is grazed down in a series of steps so that individual tillers may be grazed several times in the course of a day. The proportion of the leaf removed is likely to be high but, because of variations in the initial size of tillers and irregularities in ground contours and in the sward surface, there will be substantial variability in the amount and proportion of residual leaf on individual tillers.

Where animals have access to relatively large areas of land, and rates of herbage production and consumption are more or less in balance, individual tillers or groups of tillers are defoliated at intervals varying from 3 to 4 weeks at relatively low stocking rates to as little as 5–6 days where the stocking rate is high. The amount and proportion of the leaf tissue which is removed from a tiller will also vary. In normal circumstances the proportion of the total leaf removed at a single defoliation is unlikely to exceed 25 per cent on average but, in extreme cases, the combination of a high frequency and a high severity of defoliation can result in a rate of leaf removal equivalent to 10 per cent per day (Table 5.1), a rate which cannot be sustained for long without a marked depression in herbage growth.

It is known that simple carbohydrates can be translocated to defoliated tillers from neighbouring, undefoliated tillers, and it is reasonable to assume that this will aid the recovery growth of grazed tillers. Mutual support is likely to be more important under continuous stocking, where tillers may be grazed individually or in small clumps, than under intermittent grazing management where most of the tillers in a paddock may be defoliated in a short period. However, it is difficult to disentangle

Table 5.1   The influence of grazing treatment on the frequency and severity of defoliation of individual tillers in continuously stocked swards grazed by sheep*

	Paddock		
	1	2	3
Stocking rate (sheep per ha)	29	77	91
Herbage mass (kg DM per ha)	2940	2630	1820
Interval between defoliations (days)	10	5.5	5.5
Severity of defoliation (% of total leaf removed per defoliation)	13	38	67
% of leaf removed per day	1.3	6.1	12.2

* Measurements made on perennial ryegrass swards under continuous stocking with sheep. The very hard grazing on paddock 3 eventually led to the loss of many tillers from the sward.

this particular effect from the other differences which exist between continuously stocked and intermittently defoliated swards.

Under continuous stocking, as under intermittent defoliation, grazing tends to be concentrated in the surface layers of the sward. Thus the chances of defoliation are greater for large than for small tillers. These effects might be expected to reduce progressively the variability in size of established tillers in continuously stocked swards, but it is not clear to what extent this in fact occurs nor, in view of the continuing influx of new, small tillers, what its impact is likely to be in practice. The chances of defoliation are also greater for the two youngest leaves on a tiller than for any older leaves (Fig. 5.1), simply as a consequence of their positions in the sward canopy, though in swards where there is complete foliage cover the expanding leaves may have a greater chance of avoiding defoliation. Since the recently expanded leaf is a major contributor to the energy economy of the tiller its removal can have serious consequences for continued leaf development.

The other consequence of this pattern of grazing is that the chance of defoliation for any leaf (or part of a leaf) which has stopped elongating will decline progressively with time because it

Figure 5.1 The influence of leaf age on the chance of defoliation in a continuously stocked sward.

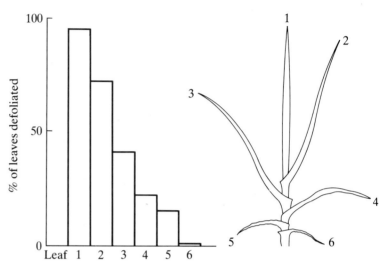

Leaves are numbered in sequence from the youngest to the oldest on a tiller. Usually only the youngest three leaves are green on vegetative tillers of perennial ryegrass. The younger leaves tend to be arranged higher in the sward canopy (though young expanding leaves may still not have penetrated into the surface layers) and this largely explains their greater chances of defoliation.

will tend to be overtopped by younger leaves, and because it will soon reach a stage where animals are reluctant to graze it even if it is exposed (Ch. 4). The major exception to this generalization occurs when animals are obliged to graze into previously untouched horizons of a sward, when substantial amounts of senescent material are likely to be removed. This effect normally occurs as a consequence of a decline in herbage growth rate caused by drought, or by low temperature in the autumn.

Where herbage production exceeds demand, animals tend to concentrate their grazing activity on particular areas of the sward and to ignore others. In these circumstances the chances of defoliation are likely to be greater for previously defoliated than for previously undefoliated tillers so that a mosaic of grazed and ungrazed patches develops. In these circumstances variability in tiller size tends to increase, and the development of seed heads can occur very quickly on ungrazed areas. Although the grazing of herbage on the grazed areas may be efficient, the overall losses of herbage on the sward as a whole will be high.

Tissue turnover in the sward

The pattern of tissue accumulation against time in a sward growing after being harvested close to ground level is often represented by the curve shown in Fig. 5.2(a). This has a slow initial phase of accumulation, a phase of accelerating accumulation and, finally, a phase in which the rate of accumulation declines to zero as the sward approaches ceiling yield (Fig. 5.2(b)). It used to be assumed that for maximum herbage production a sward should be kept, as far as possible, in the middle, rapid phase of accumulation. This would mean avoiding too frequent or severe defoliation, and avoiding too long a rest interval between defoliations. However, the curve of herbage accumulation is often much flatter than the extreme form shown in Fig. 5.2, implying a more nearly constant rate of accumulation with time. In reality, particularly in grazed swards, substantial variations in either. the frequency or severity of defoliation have remarkably little effect on the average rate of herbage accumulation over time.

The reason for this apparent discrepancy between theory and practice has to do with the fact that the rate at which herbage accumulates in a sward in the absence of grazing animals (net herbage production) represents the difference between the rate of growth of new plant tissue (often described as gross production) and the rate of loss of established tissue to senescence and decomposition (Fig. 5.3(a)). Both of these processes go on almost continuously in a normal sward. In Fig. 5.2, for example, initially the rates of both growth and loss are low; the rate of growth then accelerates but is ultimately balanced out by the later acceleration in the rate of loss to senescence as mature herbage accumulates.

The balance between the rates of growth and loss changes over time, but it is also strongly affected at any point in time by the way that the sward is managed, and this can have a marked effect upon the shape of successive accumulation curves. This is the simple situation. When grazing animals are present the net sward changes reflect the balance between the rate of net production and the rate of consumption of herbage (Fig. 5.3(b)).

The rate of herbage growth sets the potential production from a sward, but the actual amount of herbage consumed by grazing

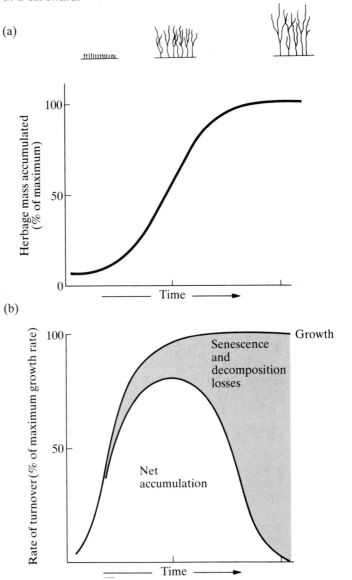

Figure 5.2 The time sequences of (a) herbage accumulation and (b) tissue turnover in a cut sward.

This is an illustration of (a) the cumulative changes in herbage mass (kilogram per hectare) in a sward over time during a period of recovery growth after a cut close to ground level, and (b) the corresponding

*changes in the rates of herbage growth, senescence and net
accumulation (kilograms per hectare per day).*

*The pattern of change with time in the rate of net herbage
accumulation following defoliation reflects the balance between changes
in the rate of growth of new plant tissue and the rate of loss of mature
tissue to senescence and decomposition. Growth rate usually increases
rapidly from a low level immediately after defoliation, and eventually
reaches an equilibrium level as the amount of green leaf in the sward
stabilizes. The losses to senescence and decomposition initially increase
more slowly, depending upon the amount of mature tissue remaining
after defoliation, but increase progressively and will eventually come to
equal the rate of growth. The rate of accumulation is low immediately
following defoliation, increases to a maximum and then declines again
to zero as the sward approaches ceiling mass. The time required to ·
reach this state depends upon the time of year and fertilizer input, but
in normal circumstances will take 6–12 weeks.*

Figure 5.3   Tissue turnover in (a) ungrazed and (b) grazed swards.

(a)

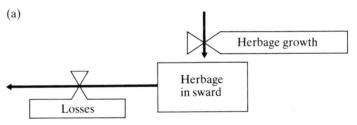

Net production = Growth − Losses to senescence and decomposition

(b)

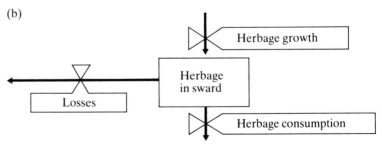

Net accumulation = Growth − [Losses + consumption]

animals represents this potential modified by the efficiency of utilization; that is, the partitioning between consumption and senescence. This may seem to be an obvious statement to make, but rates of growth, consumption and senescence tend to respond in different ways to variations in sward management, and the implications of a particular management policy to the relative efficiencies of the growing and harvesting processes are not always apparent. In order to work out these implications it is necessary first of all to understand how the individual rate processes can be controlled. In the rest of this chapter attention is concentrated on the influence of sward conditions upon herbage growth and utilization, and net herbage production, with a final section dealing with seasonal variations in production. Sward conditions are described mainly in terms of surface height and leaf area index (LAI), since these are the variables which show the most consistent influence on herbage production. Herbage consumption is considered in Chapter 7.

Herbage growth

The rate of herbage growth may be influenced by both the supply of energy from photosynthesis, reflecting the size and photosynthetic efficiency of the leaf canopy, and by the number and activity of the growth sites – grass tillers and clover growing points – per unit area of ground.

The pattern of leaf growth over time following defoliation in an intermittently cut or grazed sward will depend upon the carbohydrate reserves of the plants at the time, as well as on the severity of defoliation (Fig. 5.4). In a sward with good reserves and which is laxly defoliated the rate of leaf growth may be high initially, though the early growth of leaf is sustained at the cost of some loss of reserves from the stem base. Where reserves are low the growth rate will be low initially and will increase as the LAI increases, but at a progressively diminishing rate. Severe defoliation, resulting in the loss of most leaf tissue and possibly the death of some tillers, causes a more pronounced lag in growth until new tillers can develop to generate new leaf. This lag in regrowth occurs most commonly following a heavy cut for conservation.

On continuously stocked or frequently cut swards, where day-to-day changes are relatively small, the rate of herbage growth increases rapidly up to LAI 2–3, but tends to stabilize at higher levels of LAI and sward height (Fig. 5.5). In the phase above

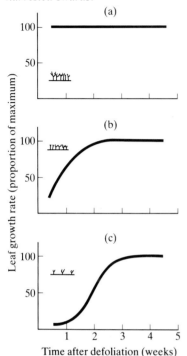

Figure 5.4 Alternative patterns of leaf growth over time in harvested swards.

In a sward with good energy reserves and where substantial amounts of leaf remain after defoliation (a), the rate of growth of new leaf may be maintained at a high level. Early leaf growth is maintained at the expense of energy reserves in tiller bases, and when these are low (b) the growth rate will also be low until enough new leaf tissue has developed to generate new energy supplies. Severe defoliation (c) which removes virtually all leaf tissue and is also likely to result in the death of some tillers, contributes to a substantial lag in growth until new tillers can develop to help to generate new leaf. Note that this figure only shows changes in the rate of leaf growth. Rates of net herbage accumulation will also be affected by the amounts of mature leaf remaining after defoliation and their contribution to senescence and decomposition losses.

LAI 3 there is a closed sward canopy which ensures complete interception of incoming light (see Fig. 3.12) and an effective balance between declining growth per tiller and increasing tiller numbers (Fig. 5.6). Below a sward height of 3 cm or LAI 2–3 the continued increase in tiller numbers is no longer adequate to offset declining growth per tiller. The effectiveness of light interception then starts to fall and eventually tiller numbers also fall (Fig. 5.6), resulting in a very rapid decline in growth rate (Fig. 5.5).

There is a similar relationship in rotationally grazed swards between severity of defoliation and herbage production (Fig. 5.7). In this case, however, adaptive sward changes are not so complete because of the marked fluctuations in sward conditions during grazing and regrowth.

When considered simply in terms of herbage growth rate, there are obvious advantages to managements which maintain sward height above 5–6 cm and LAI above 3–4 on both rotationally grazed and continuously stocked swards. These potential advantages must be set against the longer-term risks of an accumulation of dead material and reductions in tiller populations and tillering activity, particularly in continuously stocked swards which can, over the course of a season, lead to a breakdown in sward structure and a loss of growth potential. The practical implications are discussed later, but the associated effects of sward conditions on the efficiency of herbage utilization must also be considered. They are dealt with in the next section.

Figure 5.5   *The influence of sward conditions (sward surface height, LAI) upon rates of herbage growth, senescence and net production on continuously stocked swards.*

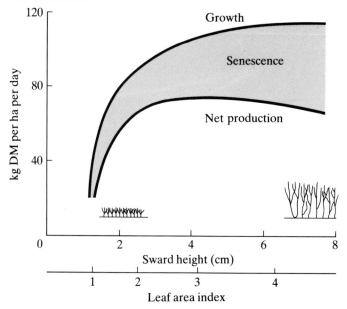

This is an illustration of the relationships between sward height or leaf area index (LAI) and rates of herbage growth, senescence and net production in a series of swards maintained in a uniform condition by grazing with ewes and lambs under continuous stocking management. The changing balance between the rates of herbage growth and senescence with increasing sward height shown here is similar to the change with time after cutting in an intermittently defoliated sward (Fig. 5.2(b)).

Utilization: herbage consumption and loss

Herbage cannot be 'stored' in a sward; most of the green leaf which is left on a tiller after defoliation is likely to be senescent by the time of the next grazing or cutting, and will not subsequently be recovered. With one or two exceptions this is a reasonable generalization. It is a consequence of the strictly limited life span of individual leaves which ensures that, once a leaf has reached maturity, the degenerative changes of senescence will start very soon. Senescent leaves are generally unacceptable to grazing animals and so are likely to be avoided. Cutting machines do not exert the same discrimination, but the basal sec-

Figure 5.6 *The influence of sward conditions under continuous stocking*
management upon tiller population density and growth per tiller.

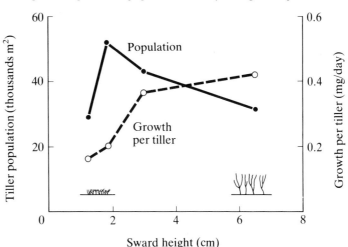

The rate of leaf growth per tiller falls steadily with decreasing sward
height over a series of continuously stocked swards. Declining growth
per tiller is counterbalanced by increasing tiller numbers at sward
heights above 2 cm, but below 2 cm the tiller population also falls,
resulting in the marked decline in herbage growth rate per hectare on
short swards shown in Fig. 5.5.

tions of leaves left behind at one harvest are likely to remain
below cutting height at the next. Individual leaves reach the
senescent stage when three younger leaves have appeared on the
same tiller. During the summer months, when growth is active,
this stage can be reached within 3 weeks from the time that a
leaf first appears from the sheath tube of older leaves. Any leaf
will therefore have only one chance of defoliation before the
onset of senescence in a normal 3- or 4-week grazing cycle, and
no more than two chances even under heavy continuous stocking
where, on average, tillers may be grazed every 7–10 days.

Over a period of time the rate of tissue loss to senescence and
decomposition increases in direct proportion to the average mass
of herbage maintained in the sward. This is illustrated for continuously stocked swards in Fig. 5.5. Following an efficient
grazing under rotational management the time required for new
leaves to reach this stage of maturity means that there is a lag

Figure 5.7   *The influence of grazing management on rates of herbage growth, senescence and net production on rotationally grazed swards.*

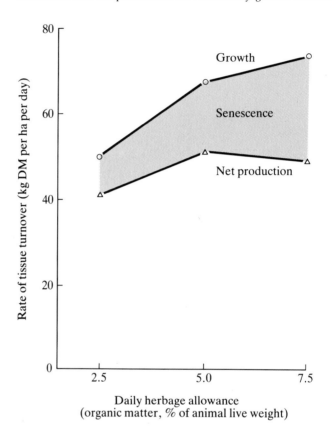

This is an illustration of the relationship between the daily allowance of herbage to animals under rotational grazing management and the rates of tissue turnover in the sward. Daily herbage allowance controls the severity of defoliation of the sward at each grazing–the lower the allowance the more severe the defoliation and the less the residual herbage remaining after grazing. The association between the rates of herbage growth and senescence, and the effect upon net herbage production, are therefore similar to the patterns shown in Fig. 5.5 for continuously stocked swards. The rates of tissue turnover shown are mean values over the regrowth period between one grazing and the next in a 3-week cycle in a perennial ryegrass sward grazed by dairy cows.

before senescence losses are observed. However here, too, there is a proportionate relationship between herbage mass and rate of senescence over a series of 'grazings (Fig. 5.7). Thus, the relatively high levels of herbage mass and LAI which must be maintained to ensure high herbage growth rates inevitably result in high senescence losses.

This is not necessarily to suggest that all senescence losses are a bad thing. The important criterion is the amount of herbage *harvested* per unit area. There is good evidence to indicate, for grazed swards at least, that the highest rate of net herbage production is unlikely to be achieved either by a management which maximizes growth rate or by one which minimizes the rate of loss. Complete efficiency of recovery of all herbage grown is not possible in any grassland system, but there is scope for controlling losses. The combination of a growth rate which increases at a steadily diminishing rate and a senescence rate which increases linearly dictates that the rate of net herbage production per hectare will stabilize at levels of LAI and sward height well below those which maximize growth rate (Figs 5.5 and 5.7).

Checks and balances

In summary, the evidence considered in the earlier sections of this chapter indicates that a number of compromises have to be made in order to achieve high rates of herbage consumption per unit area from grazed swards. Compromises are necessary: (a) between the requirements for effective light interception and high photosynthetic efficiency in the sward; (b) between the conditions for high current growth rates and those for the maintenance of a vigorous tiller population to safeguard future growth capability; and (c) between the requirements for high growth rates and low rates of loss to senescence and decomposition. Under continuous stocking management the best compromise between these conflicting demands is achieved by maintaining a sward at an average LAI of about 3, equivalent to a sward only 3–4 cm high (Fig. 5.5). A similar optimum mean LAI is indicated for rotationally grazed swards, though in this case there is considerable fluctuation about the mean during periods of grazing and regrowth. It is now clear, too, that deliberate manipulation of sward state or intermittent grazing will not improve rates of herbage growth and net production over those achieved under continuous stocking management with the same fertilizer inputs, except perhaps during periods of reproductive growth in spring.

Despite the conclusions that rates of net herbage production are maximized at relatively low levels of sward height and LAI, adaptive changes in tiller populations and in the balance between leaf growth and loss per tiller ensure that net herbage production is remarkably stable over a substantial range of sward conditions. This has important practical advantages because it allows considerable room for manoeuvre about the theoretical optimum conditions with little detriment to herbage production. The implications of this conclusion will be apparent when the influence of sward conditions on the herbage intake of grazing animals is considered in Chapter 7.

The results shown in Figs 5.5 and 5.7 relate specifically to swards dominated by perennial ryegrass, a species which maintains relatively high tiller populations and high rates of leaf turnover, in a humid temperate climate. The same principles would be expected to apply to other grass species with similar characteristics, and to a wider range of climatic conditions, though detailed information is not available. However, the sward conditions optimizing the balance between rates of growth and senescence may well differ for species which characteristically maintain smaller populations of larger tillers (Ch. 11).

Seasonal variations in herbage production

The typical seasonal pattern of net herbage production in a cut grass sward in the UK is illustrated in Fig. 5.8. This pattern fol-

Figure 5.8   *Typical seasonal patterns of herbage production in grass and clover swards in the UK.*

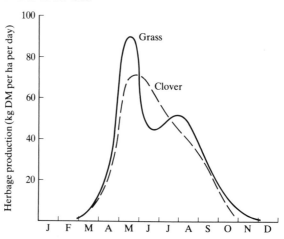

This is an illustration of the contrasts between the seasonal patterns of herbage production in grass and clover swards in the UK. The contrasts apply across a range of conditions, but the details of each pattern depend upon variations in the length of the growing season, the duration and severity of summer drought, the pattern of fertilizer application (Ch. 12) and the plant species used (Ch. 11).

The curves relate to plots of grass and clover grown separately under irrigation in the south of England, and cut at monthly intervals. The grass, which was S23 perennial ryegrass, received generous fertilizer applications at frequent intervals. The clover was S100 white clover, and received no fertilizer N.

lows approximately the seasonal fluctuations in temperature and light intensity in a temperate climate, though the relationship is distorted to some degree by the high net production rates in spring which are associated with reproductive growth (Ch. 3) and

Figure. 5.9   Seasonal pattern of herbage production under continuous stocking management.

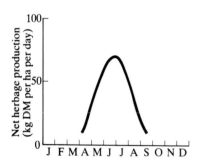

This is an illustration of the seasonal variations in the rate of net herbage production from a perennial ryegrass dominated sward in central Scotland which was stocked with sheep to maintain a sward surface height of 3–4 cm and received nitrogenous fertilizer at the rate of 20 kg N per hectare every 3 weeks. In these circumstances net herbage production is equivalent to the amount harvested by the sheep, and can be compared directly with the estimates of herbage harvested under a monthly cutting management shown in Fig. 5.8, which is drawn to the same scale. Note the more uniform pattern of herbage production under continuous stocking, and the absence of the pronounced spring peak (which is usually associated with seed-head development) and the succeeding summer trough in the cut grass sward.

The shorter period of herbage production in Fig. 5.9 than in Fig. 5.8 reflects the shorter grazing season in Scotland than in the south of England.

by the relatively low rates in summer which may be due to a combination of water deficit and, in some cases, a decline in tiller population following the loss of reproductive tillers. The pattern of growth over the growing season in a continuously stocked sward is much more uniform (Fig. 5.9), particularly where spring grazing is severe enough to prevent the development of flowering tillers.

Active growth occurs at a temperature of 5–6°C in perennial ryegrass but at a slightly higher temperature in clover, so growth starts later in the spring in clover than in the grasses. However, clover usually has a more consistent pattern of growth through the summer months than the grasses (Fig. 5.8). The winter temperature in the UK is seldom low enough to prevent grass growth altogether except for limited periods of time. However, over this period the low rate of herbage growth is more or less balanced by senescence losses, so that the rates of herbage accumulation in an undisturbed sward will be close to zero for some weeks. In New Zealand, the rate of herbage accumulation in winter may vary from 0 to 30 kg dry matter per hectare per day, reflecting the influence of latitude and altitude on winter temperatures.

Animal effects

So far herbage growth and utilization have been discussed in terms which imply a uniform pattern of defoliation, but this is seldom completely true under grazing conditions. The patchy distribution of dung and urine contribute to unevenness in herbage growth; the patchy grazing which follows results in uneven utiliz-

Table 5.2 *The relative proportions of areas of closely grazed and laxly grazed herbage in swards under continuous stocking management with cattle or sheep, and sward heights on closely and laxly grazed areas**

	Cattle	Sheep
Proportion of area (%)		
Close grazed	72	61
Lax grazed	28	39
Sward surface height (cm) on:		
Close-grazed areas	3.0	3.0
Lax-grazed areas	4.4	4.3

* These results refer to measurements made in early autumn on swards maintained at similar heights under continuous stocking with either cattle or sheep. When swards are managed similarly, the proportion of the total area closely grazed at any time by cattle and sheep is similar. The results indicate that sward heights on close-grazed and lax-grazed areas were similar for the two species, though earlier in the year the sward height on lax-grazed areas would be expected to be greater on cattle swards than on sheep swards.

ation, and tends to be self-perpetuating because of the accumulation of mature herbage in ungrazed areas. Low overall efficiency of herbage utilization itself tends to result in the formation of seed heads and patchy grazing irrespective of the presence of excreta. Subsequently animals will tend to ignore mature herbage, resulting in high senscence losses. However, it is difficult to be certain whether uneven grazing has any major influence in itself upon herbage production, as distinct from being a symptom of poor utilization. The implications of these effects to thinking about grazing management are considered in Chapters 13 and 15.

Figure 5.10   *Tiller populations and tissue turnover in swards grazed by cattle and sheep, alone and in combination.*

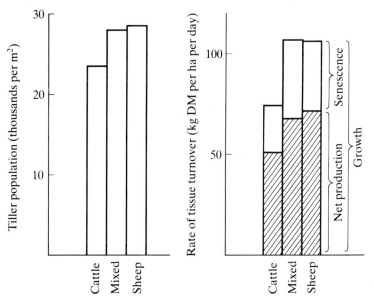

These comparisons relate to swards which were maintained under continuous stocking by cattle and sheep, alone and in combination. Mean values are shown for swards maintained at 3 and 4.5 cm for most of the grazing season. Cattle grazing depressed tiller population and rates of herbage growth and net production. Tiller populations and rates of tissue turnover in swards grazed by mixed groups of sheep and cattle (in the ratio of 3:1) were similar to those in swards grazed by sheep alone.

Sheep-grazed swards usually appear to be less variable than cattle-grazed swards, although animal species effects are often confused by differences in sward management. Where comparisons are made between swards which are managed similarly, the relative proportions of closely grazed and laxly grazed herbage on swards grazed by cattle and sheep are similar (Table 5.2), though the undergrazed patches are smaller and more numerous on sheep than on cattle swards and sward height in the ungrazed patches may be lower. Rates of tiller loss are greater under cattle grazing than sheep grazing, so sheep-grazed swards develop higher tiller populations than equivalent cattle-grazed swards and this results in higher rates of herbage growth and net production. Swards grazed by mixed groups of sheep and cattle have tiller populations and rates of herbage production and utilization similar to those under grazing by sheep alone (Fig. 5.10).

Chapter 6   Plant composition and nutritive value

The rate of growth in a growing animal and the milk yield of a lactating animal depend first upon the intake of nutrients, and second upon the efficiency of conversion of ingested nutrients into body tissue or milk. Nutrient intake itself is the product of the amount of herbage eaten and the concentration of nutrients in that herbage:

Nutrient intake = Herbage intake × Nutrient concentration
Herbage intake and food conversion efficiency are considered in Chapters 7 and 8. In this chapter attention is focused on the factors influencing the nutrient content of herbage, but it is important to bear in mind that the three variables are closely interlinked.

The concentrations of the main organic constituents of plant tissue, the compounds of carbon and nitrogen, are principally a function of plant maturity. However, the concentrations of the mineral constituents (including nitrogen) also reflect the mineral status of the soil and the supply of fertilizer nutrients, and are influenced by the botanical composition of the sward. An indication of the range of variation in some of the more important constituents of herbage is given in Table 6.1. The nutritive value of the organic components is influenced by the ease with which they can be digested and incorporated into bacterial tissue, and the site of digestion and absorption in the alimentary tract.

Similarly, the value of the mineral constituents will be determined by their solubility and ease of absorption. In most circumstances the major determinant of animal performance is likely to be the intake of utilizable energy, generally expressed in terms of metabolizable energy, ME (Fig. 6.1). The concentration of ME is closely related to the digestibility of organic matter, and the digestibility of herbage has an important influence upon the amount eaten in many circumstances.

Figure 6.1   The digestion and metabolism of dietary energy in ruminant animals.

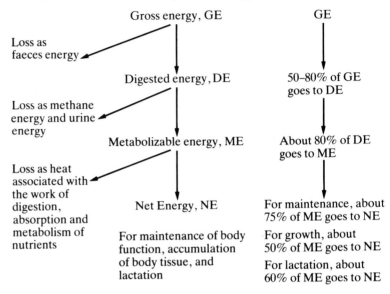

The digestibility of the gross energy varies widely, depending mainly upon the maturity of the herbage, but the ratio of metabolizable to digestible energy is very consistent. The efficiency of utilization of ME for maintenance of body function is higher than that for lactation, and the efficiency of use for body tissue accumulation is lowest of all. The priority of use of ME for these three major functions is also in the order maintenance–lactation–body tissue. The ME of a feed is normally expressed in terms of an energy concentration (megajoules per kilogram of dry matter, MJ/Kg DM).

The digestibility and ME values of herbage are closely related. For example, at normal levels of N concentration in plant tissues, equivalent levels of organic matter digestibility (OMD) and ME are:

OMD (%)	ME (MJ/kg DM)
50	6.5
60	9.0
70	10.5
80	12.0

Herbage is seldom a 'balanced' diet in the sense that its organic and inorganic constituents are present in the concentrations and proportions which best meet the needs of animals. For most forms of animal production, for example, there is often a surplus of nitrogenous components in young herbage, and a deficiency in mature herbage (Table 6.1).

Usually, the concentration of the simple and readily soluble nitrogenous compounds is too high for them to be efficiently utilized, and imbalances in the concentrations of the mineral constituents of herbage can lead to subclinical or clinical metabolic disturbances. Many of these imbalances can be corrected by the judicious use of dietary supplements but, with certain specific exceptions (see Ch. 14), the use of supplements for this purpose is seldom justified under grazing conditions.

Table 6.1   The ranges of concentration of some of the organic and inorganic constitutents of herbage, and necessary concentrations to meet the requirements of sheep and cattle

	Normal range in herbage	Desirable herbage content for:	
		Fattening sheep	Lactating cows
Nutrient			
Metabolizable energy (MJ/kg DM)	8–12	10.5	10.5
Crude protein* (g/kg DM)	100–250	110	110
Mineral element (g/kg DM)			
Calcium	2–10	4	4
Phosphorus	2–5	2	3
Sodium	0.5–10	1	1
Magnesium	1–4	1	2

* Crude protein = Nitrogen × 6.25.
From Agricultural Research Council (1980) *The Nutrient Requirements of Ruminant Livestock.* Commonwealth Agricultural Bureaux, Farnham Royal; MAFF, DAFS and DANI (1975) *Energy Allowances and Feeding Systems for Ruminants.* Technical Bulletin 33, HMSO; Osbourn, D. F. (1980) The feeding value of grass and grass products. In *Grass: Its Production and Utilization* (ed. W. Holmes). Blackwell Scientific Publications.

The desirable concentrations shown are for 30 kg lambs growing at about 150 g/day, and for Friesian cows yielding about 20 kg milk per day.

The contents of living cells consist principally of relatively simple compounds of carbon and nitrogen, and are readily digested. The cell walls are composed of more complex compounds – cellulose and hemicellulose – which are less digestible than the cell contents and which become increasingly lignified and less digestible with age. The effect of the progressive increases in the ratio of cell walls to cell contents and in the degree of lignification of the cell walls is that the digestibility of leaf tissue falls from a level of 80–90 per cent in young, expanding leaves to around 70 per cent in mature leaves. The decline in digestibility continues as leaves start to lose cell contents with advancing senescence, so that the digestibility of dead leaf tissue declines to 40–50 per cent. Similar changes take place in the leaf sheaths of vegetative tillers (Fig. 6.2). The extending flowering stem is initially as digestible as leaf tissue, but it quickly becomes heavily lignified so that its digestibility falls more rapidly and to even lower levels than that of leaf and sheath tissues (Fig. 6.2).

The ratio of stem to leaf increases rapidly with time in a reproductive sward in the spring (Fig. 6.3). This, coupled with the changes in each of the main components, results in the characteristic pattern of decline in digestibility with increasing maturity in grass swards (Fig. 6.4). Once the reproductive phase of growth is completed the changes in digestibility with increasing sward maturity are less marked. There are differences between grass species and cultivars in the pattern of change in digestibility, both during spring growth (Fig. 6.4) and later in the year. These are explained by differences in the relative proportions of leaf and stem on the plant and in the digestibility of these components at equivalent stages of maturity. They may also be due to differences in the timing of seed-head development in the spring. The onset of flowering can be influenced to some degree by spring temperatures; information on dates of spring flowering and on projected effects on forage digestibility is usually available from extension agencies.

White clover maintains a higher digestibility than the grasses because the amount of structural tissue in the plant is lower, and probably because dead tissue tends to disappear more quickly than from a grass sward (Fig. 6.4). The clovers have a lower content of cell walls than the grasses at comparable stages of growth.

Figure 6.4 shows a substantial decline in digestibility over a 6–8-week period of primary growth in the spring. However, in

Figure 6.2   *Changes in the digestibility of individual plant components with increasing maturity:* (———) *leaf blade;* (- - -) *leaf sheath;* (—·—·—) *flowering stem. From Terry, R. A. and Tilley, J. M. A. (1964) J. Br. Grassld Soc., 19, 363–72.*

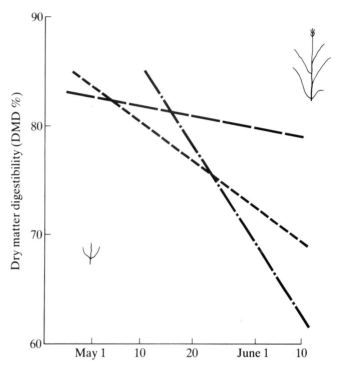

This is an illustration of changes in the digestibility of the component parts of perennial ryegrass plants over a period of uninterrupted growth in the spring. Patterns for other grass species are similar. Figure 6.4 illustrates changes in the digestibility of the complete sward with increasing maturity, reflecting changes in the relative proportions of the different plant parts (Fig. 6.3) as well as in their digestibility.

Throughout this book digestibility is expressed in terms of the percentage (%) of the dry matter or organic matter of herbage which is digested (DMD or OMD). Digestibility may also be expressed in terms of the percentage of digestible organic matter in the feed dry matter (DOMD or D-value). This expression is frequently used in ruminant nutrition because it is closely related to the energy value of a feed, but it is unnecessarily complicated for most herbage intake work. Because of the way it is calculated, the DOMD of a forage is normally about 90 per cent of the DMD or OMD.

Figure 6.3   Changes with maturity in the proportions of leaf and stem tissue in a reproductive sward. From Wilman, D., Ojuederic, B. M. and Asare, E. O. (1976) J. Br. Grassld Soc., 31, 73–9.

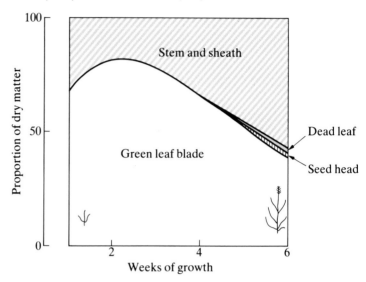

The 'stem and sheath' fraction includes true reproductive stems and the leaf sheaths surrounding the tiller bases. The results relate to a sward growing towards seeding in the spring.

perennial ryegrass swards which are grazed at intervals no greater than 3–4 weeks, the digestibility of the herbage eaten should remain above 70 per cent for the duration of the growing season so long as residual herbage is not left at one grazing to dilute the value of new growth at the next. In a continuously stocked sward which is efficiently grazed, where the animals are consistently eating young leaf material, the digestibility of the herbage consumed should also remain at a high level (Fig. 6.5).

The arrangement of plant components within a sward canopy means that the digestibility of successive layers of herbage within the sward is likely to decline with increasing proximity to ground level. The pattern of digestibility distribution will depend upon the way in which the sward has been managed, however. Figure 6.6 is typical of a sward cut or grazed regularly, in which senescent material has been accumulated below the height of defoliation. In a continuously stocked sward there is likely to be a steady change in digestibility from the top to the bottom of the canopy.

Figure 6.4   Changes with increasing maturity in the digestibility of herbage harvested from grass and clover swards. From Green, J. O., Corrall, A. J. and Terry, R. A. (1971) Grass species and varieties; relationships between stage of growth, yield and forage quality. Grassland Research Institute. Technical Report No. 8.

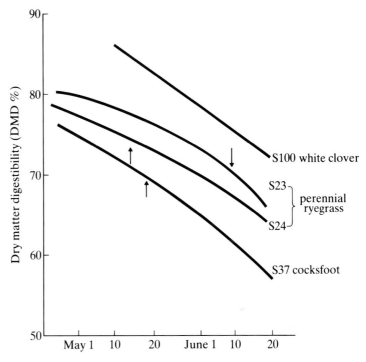

These examples illustrate differences in digestibility at similar dates between: (a) two varieties of perennial ryegrass; (b) the ryegrasses and a variety of cocksfoot; and (c) the grasses and white clover. The arrows indicate heading dates for the grasses.

Changes in herbage digestibility with increasing maturity are paralleled by changes in nitrogen (N) content. Typically the N content of the dry matter (DM) of young herbage is in the range 3–4 per cent, declining to as low as 1 per cent in very mature herbage. The crude protein content is calculated by multiplying the N content by 6.25, giving an extreme range of crude protein content from 6 to 25 per cent. In young herbage, however, particularly where heavy applications of nitrogenous fertilizer

Figure 6.5 *Seasonal variations in the digestibility of the herbage consumed from well-managed swards by grazing animals.*

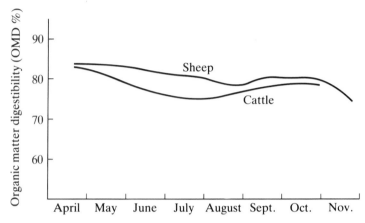

The lines shown refer: (a) to ewes under continuous stocking management; and (b) to dairy cows under rotational grazing management. The herbage eaten by the ewes declines in digestibility after weaning in July as a result of a period of hard grazing, and again in November as the sward is eaten down to winter levels.

have been used, much of the N may be present in the form of relatively simple compounds. At N concentrations below 1 per cent in the DM the fermentative efficiency of the rumen bacteria may be impaired, reducing herbage intake and digestion. Limiting N concentrations of this order are unlikely to be reached in temperate swards except in unusual conditions. The N content of the foliage of legume plants is usually higher than that of the grasses at low levels of use of fertilizer N. Nitrogenous fertilizer itself causes a marked increase in herbage N concentration with no marked effect upon the energy value of the herbage.

Levels of digestibility and N content are generally lower in tropical pastures than in temperate pastures, and rates of decline with increasing maturity are greater. These differences appear to be linked to the generally higher temperatures under which tropical pastures grow.

The total concentration of the inorganic constituents of herbage – the ash content – normally lies in the range 5–12 per cent. Much of this content is made up of plant silica which is of no nutritional importance. However, contamination with soil can

Figure 6.6   The variation in digestibility with height in a sward canopy.

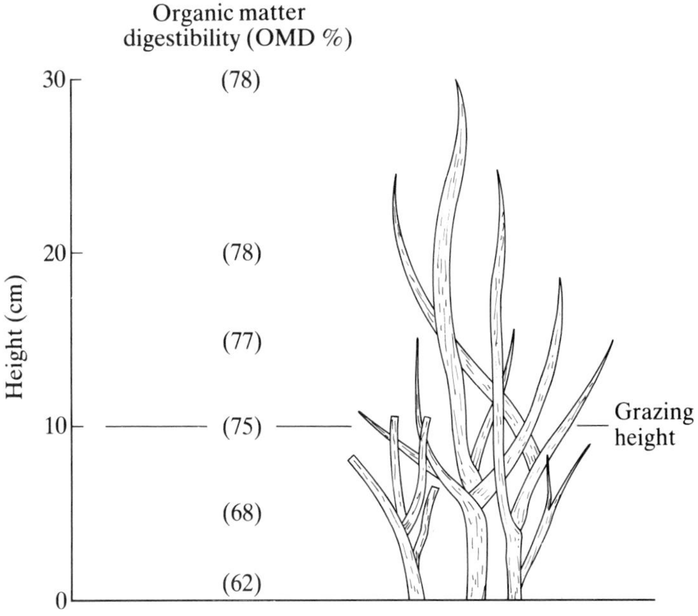

The sward has been grazed regularly to a height of about 10 cm. The accumulation of old tiller stubs and dead leaf material below this level depresses herbage digestibility, but above it most of the herbage consists of fresh leaf.

readily increase the ash content of herbage to 20 per cent, and even to 40–50 per cent in extreme conditions. This may increase the intake of essential minerals, but it will also reduce the concentration of the major nutrients and can lead to a depression in the amount of herbage eaten. The presence of variable amounts of soil contamination on herbage can confuse measurements of nutrient intake by grazing animals. This is why most of the estimates of herbage intake quoted in the next chapter are expressed in terms of organic matter – that is, after correcting for the content of both soil and plant minerals.

The water content of herbage comes from two sources: that bound within the plant, mainly in the cell contents, which is only released when herbage is chewed and the cell walls ruptured; and surface water from rain or dew. The water content declines with increasing maturity from about 80 to 70 per cent in surface-dry herbage, but can be well over 90 per cent in young herbage after rain.

The performance of grazing animals is often lower in the autumn than in the spring, even on swards which are ostensibly similar in botanical composition and digestibility. This may be due in part to a lower herbage intake in the autumn, related to a greater degree of contamination from dung and soil and, possibly, to a lower DM content, but the nutritive value per unit of digestible herbage eaten may also be adversely affected by these factors and by the low ratio of readily available energy to N in the herbage at that time of the year.

Chapter 7   Herbage intake

Herbage intake is influenced by three main groups of factors:

1. Those affecting herbage digestion, relating mainly to the maturity and nutrient concentration of the herbage eaten;
2. Those affecting herbage ingestion, relating mainly to the physical structure of the sward canopy;
3. Those affecting the demand for nutrients and the digestive capacity and eating capability of the animals concerned, reflecting largely their maturity and productive state.

These groups of factors are dealt with in turn before considering the ways in which they may interact with one another to control herbage intake under grazing conditions.

Herbage composition and intake

In simple volumetric terms the ability of the alimentary tract to accommodate more food is directly related to the extent of digestion, the rate at which the products of digestion are absorbed, and the rate at which undigested residues pass through the tract. These three variables are to some degree related in unprocessed forages, and their effects on food intake tend to reinforce one another. The food intake of animals eating mixed diets of concentrates and forage may be limited by their ability to utilize fully the products of digestion, so that intake is ultimately subject to metabolic limitations. In monogastric animals like the pig, appetite control will often function in this way. For grazing animals, however, and for animals offered unprocessed forages indoors, this metabolic limit does not seem to be important. The result is that, other things being equal, food intake increases at a more or less constant rate over the full range of digestibility values likely to be encountered in practice (Fig. 7.1). Thus an improvement in herbage digestibility confers a double advantage on the grazing

Figure 7.1 The relationship between the digestibility of grazed herbage and the amount eaten.

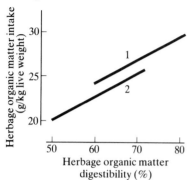

This is an illustration of the relationship between the digestibility of the herbage consumed and the amount eaten by growing calves grazing a series of first growths (line 1) or of regrowths following cutting (line 2) on a perennial ryegrass sward. The higher intake at any given digestibility for line 1 is probably associated with the more erect habit and taller growth of spring herbage. Note that the digestibility of the herbage consumed will normally be higher than that of the whole sward (Fig. 7.6).

animal: it results in an increase in the nutrient concentration of the diet and, at the same time, an increase in the quantity eaten.

The relationship between diet digestibility and intake is not necessarily a simple one, because different plant species or components can differ in their rate of digestion at similar levels of digestibility. For example, the legumes have a lower ratio of cell wall (structural) material to cell contents than the grasses at any given level of digestibility, so both the rate of digestion and the amount eaten are usually higher in legumes than in grasses. Also, diets consisting largely of plant stems are eaten in smaller quantities than diets of leaves of similar digestibility, because the structure of the stems means that they are digested more slowly.

Because the digestibility of plant tissue declines progressively with age, intake would be expected to decline progressively with increasing herbage maturity. This is normally the case for animals fed cut herbage or dried forage indoors but, under grazing conditions, parallel changes in the structure of the sward canopy can influence the relationship. In some circumstances herbage intake may be limited by a frank deficiency of dietary nitrogen; this can be a common occurrence on tropical pastures but it is rare among grazing animals on even the most mature of temperate swards.

The influence of the water content of herbage on dry matter (DM) intake is not easy to measure, and it would be easy to attach too much importance to this effect. Certainly a depression in DM intake occurs when animals are suddenly offered a feed of wet herbage, or of wetted hay or silage, but the effect tends to be transitory if the wet feed is offered continuously. The mechanisms for extracting surplus water from the digestive tract are efficient, and the adverse effects of grazing herbage with a high moisture content are, on the whole, likely to be small.

It is often suggested that herbage intake may be affected by the palatability of the material on offer. 'Palatability' is a difficult attribute to describe and even more difficult to measure, except in a relative sense. For this reason the term 'preference' was used in Chapter 4 to describe choice between the different components of a sward. Preference will influence grazing behaviour and diet composition where choice is possible, but this does not necessarily mean that 'preferred' plants will be eaten in greater quantity than 'non-preferred' plants where each is offered in isolation, as in swards containing only one species or cultivar for example. Given the present state of understanding, the possible effects of palatability differences upon herbage intake cannot be discounted, but in many circumstances the effects are likely to be small.

Grazing behaviour and herbage intake

The structure and the botanical composition of the sward canopy can exert a direct effect upon the herbage intake of grazing animals, quite apart from the influence of the chemical composition and nutrient content of the herbage itself.

The amount of herbage eaten daily is the product of the time spent grazing and the rate of herbage intake during grazing (Fig. 7.2). Rate of intake is the product of the rate of biting and the amount of herbage in each individual bite. This is a somewhat mechanistic way of looking at grazing behaviour, but herbage intake can be influenced by variations in any of these parameters. Intake per bite is very sensitive to variations in sward conditions, particularly to variations in sward height (Fig. 7.3). When intake per bite is reduced there will be a corresponding fall in the rate of intake unless there is a compensatory increase in the rate of biting. Daily herbage intake will also be adversely affected unless any reduction in rate of intake can be offset by an increase in grazing time. In practice, both biting rate and grazing time frequently do tend to increase when intake per bite falls, but these changes are seldom large enough to prevent a fall in daily herbage intake (Fig. 7.4). A grazing time in excess of 8–9 hours/day is likely to be indicative of limiting sward conditions. On extremely short swards intake per bite, rate of biting and grazing time may all decline together.

Animals tend to concentrate their grazing activity within sward layers containing mainly leaf material, and the increase in the depth of grazing with increasing sward height parallels an increase in the depth of the leafy layers in the sward (Fig. 7.5). This effect results in an increase in the volume and weight of herbage in-

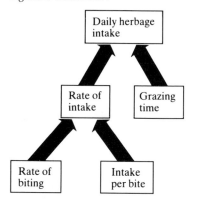

Figure 7.2   The components of ingestive behaviour.

Figure 7.3   The relationship between the surface height of the grazed sward and intake per bite.

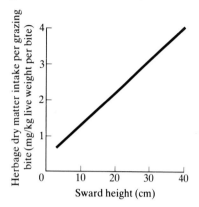

This result comes from a study with strip-grazed calves. Intake per bite expressed in this way is roughly comparable for cattle and sheep. A value of 2 mg DM per kilogram is equivalent to an intake per bite of 0.1 g of herbage DM for a 50 kg sheep, or 1 g for a 500 kg cow. In many cases intake per bite is substantially lower than this (see Fig. 7.4).

gested per bite (Fig. 7.3). The greater intake on first-growth than on second-growth swards at equivalent levels of digestibility (Fig. 7.1) is probably attributable to the more erect growth habit and greater canopy height of first of growth swards. Intake per bite and rate of intake may also increase as the bulk density of herbage (weight per unit volume) within the sward canopy increases, because the weight of herbage consumed for a given bite volume increases with increasing bulk density.

These results relate principally to intensively managed vegetative swards with a high leaf content. In swards at a reproductive stage of growth, giving a more heterogeneous mixture of leaves and stems at all levels, the overall height of the sward can still influence ingestive behaviour but the relative proportions of leaves and stems also become important because of the effects upon selective grazing behaviour. In these circumstances discrimination between leaves and stems, or between live and dead tissue, means that the digestibility of the diet selected is likely to be greater than that of the sward as a whole. This effect is greater in sheep than in cattle (Fig. 7.6). It increases the nutrient concentration of the diet and would therefore be expected to increase intake. However, intake per bite, rate of biting and rate of intake tend to fall progressively with increasing intensity of selection so selective grazing does not necessarily result automatically in a higher level of nutrient intake. The same arguments apply to mixed swards, where between–species selection is likely to result in a reduction in the rate of herbage intake.

The relationships shown in Figs 7.1 and 7.3 are reasonably clear-cut, but it is not always easy to determine the influence of particular sward characteristics on ingestive behaviour because many of them tend to change together. Sward height and herbage bulk density are often inversely related, for example, both within a sward as it is grazed down and between swards. The behavioural responses shown in Fig. 7.4 probably reflect the dominant influence of height in the swards concerned, but this

Figure 7.4 *The relationships between sward height and (a) intake per bite; (b) rate of biting; (c) grazing time, and (d) daily herbage intake, illustrating the dominant influence of intake per bite on daily herbage intake. From Penning, P. D. (1985) In Grazing research at northern latitudes. Proceedings of NATO Workshop, Iceland, pp. 219–26.*

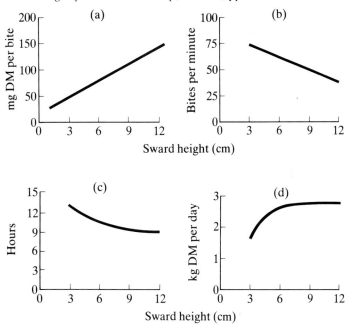

Herbage intake per bite (a) decreases progressively, and biting rate (b) and grazing time (c) tend to increase with declining sward height. At heights below 6–8 cm the increases in biting rate and grazing time are not sufficient to offset the effect of reductions in intake per bite, so daily herbage intake (d) is depressed. The decline in intake is particularly serious at sward heights below 3–4 cm.

These results were derived from groups of sheep on continuously stocked swards.

may not always be the case. Also, sward height and herbage mass will increase and herbage digestibility decline as a sward grows to maturity, with conflicting effects on ingestive behaviour and herbage intake.

Animal characteristics and herbage intake

Animals differing in production potential eat different amounts of the same herbage. Thus, lactating animals eat more than non-

Figure 7.5 The relationship between sward surface height and the depth of grazing within the sward canopy.

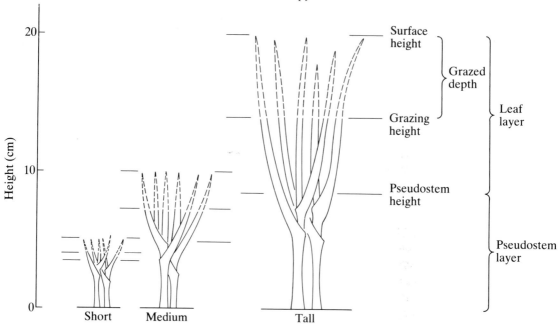

These results came from studies with grazing sheep, and illustrate the way in which the depth of the layer of vegetation encompassed at a bite is related to the overall depth of the sward canopy. A tall sward would normally be grazed down in a series of steps of progressively diminishing depth.

The depth of the basal layer of the sward containing pseudostem (actually a concentric series of leaf sheaths in vegetative tillers) increases progressively with increasing sward surface height. Normally sheep will graze readily within the leaf layer, but they show more reluctance to graze into the pseudostem layer.

These results relate to vegetative swards in which the leaf and pseudostem normally occupy different layers. In reproductive swards, where seed stems or heads are present throughout the sward canopy, more selection will occur within the leaf layer and bite dimensions are less easy to measure.

Figure 7.6   *The relationship between the digestibility of herbage in the sward and that selected by (a) calves and (b) lambs.*

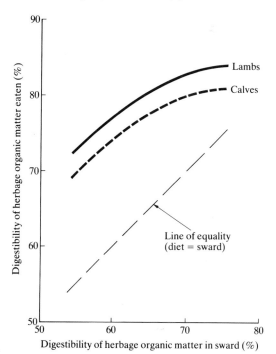

This is an illustration of the relationship between the mean digestibility of the whole sward and the digestibility of the herbage selected from it in lambs and calves grazing on a series of different swards under continuous stocking management. The difference between the digestibility of the sward and that of the diet is greater on swards containing much senescent material, and therefore of low digestibility, than it is on swards made up largely of green leaf and with a high digestibility. The lambs consistently selected a diet with a digestibility about three units higher than that selected by calves. The interpretation of this kind of evidence in terms of selective grazing activity was discussed in Chapter 4.

The degree of selection taking place is indicated by the differences between the response lines shown and the line of equality, where diet digestibility and sward digestibility are equal. However, remember that in Chapter 4 the point was made that differences in composition between sward and diet do not necessarily imply deliberate selection: they may simply reflect variations in digestibility from top to bottom of the sward canopy.

lactating animals, and young, rapidly growing animals more per unit live weight than mature animals with little growth potential (Fig 7.7).

Differences between animals in intake per bite, rate of biting and grazing time may all contribute to differences in intake. Sheep tend to have a lower biting rate than cattle and to spend more time grazing, though the differences are small and are not always consistent. The lower biting rate is probably associated with the greater selectivity of grazing by sheep in most circumstances (Fig. 7.6). Also, in taller swards sheep usually tend to graze further into the sward canopy than do cattle. Herbage intake increases rapidly in young weaned animals, in parallel with increasing grazing activity, and may reach a plateau, relative to live weight, within 3–6 weeks of weaning. The herbage intake achieved before weaning will be influenced by the level of milk intake and the age of the animal.

Figure 7.7   *The influence of sward conditions on the herbage intake of: (a) lactating cows; (b) in-calf heifers; and (c) weaned calves.*

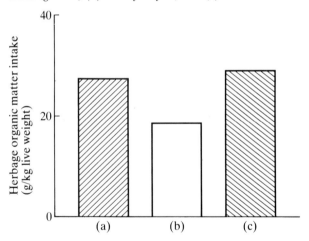

This is an illustration of the mean herbage intakes of lactating cows, pregnant heifers and calves measured over a series of swards in one year. Herbage intakes are expressed in terms of intake per unit of live weight to allow comparison between groups of animals differing substantially in live weight. The herbage intakes of the calves and lactating cows were similar, and substantially higher than the intakes of in-calf heifers.

Whatever the basic differences in diet selection, ingestive behaviour or herbage intake, different classes of livestock respond in much the same way to changes in sward conditions. This point is illustrated in the comparison between the digestibilities of the diets selected by sheep and cattle (Fig. 7.6). With some specific exceptions, this appears to be a reasonable generalization. The exceptions are for particularly short swards, where sheep may be able to maintain herbage intake better than cattle and where small animals of a species may be better able to do so than larger animals. Responses to changes in sward conditions can be unstable and unpredictable for young animals which are still learning to graze.

Within and between groups, animals with a higher level of performance tend to be those with a higher level of intake, though it is not easy to decide whether high intake is a cause or a consequence of high performance. Herbage intake from a sward will increase roughly in proportion to the nutrient requirements of the animals concerned, except in cases where intake is limited by a frank deficiency of a specific nutrient. Thus it is not correct to describe a sward in terms of a fixed production capability. For

Figure 7.8 The influence of milk yield on herbage intake and nutrient requirements in grazing dairy cows.

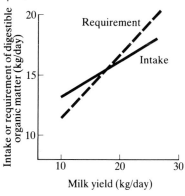

This is an illustration of the influence of milk yield on herbage intake in grazing dairy cows, and relates intake to estimates of nutrient requirements for lactating animals. Intakes and nutrient requirements are both quoted in terms of digestible organic matter for ease of comparison. The example relates to cows eating herbage with an organic matter digestibility of 75 per cent, equivalent to an ME content of about 11 MJ/kg of DM. The requirements shown make allowance for a weight gain of 0.5 kg/day. The surplus energy intake of the low-yielding cows will result in a higher rate of gain than this; the deficit for higher-yielding cows means that there will be little energy available for weight recovery, and that body reserves may be needed to sustain milk yield. An increase in the digestibility of the diet will result in the intake line moving upwards and the requirements line moving downwards, so the break-even point where the lines intersect will move towards higher yield. A decline in diet digestibility will reverse the movements.

Note that the intake response shown is an average for groups of cows; individual animals may show substantial deviations from the mean.

example, a dairy cow producing 25 litres of milk per day will eat more grass than a cow yielding 15 litres/day whatever the sward conditions. However, the degree to which energy intake fails to meet the requirements for the level of production stipulated will usually be greater in the higher-yielding animal, and will increase as the nutrient content of the herbage or the structural characteristics of the sward restrict nutrient intake (Fig. 7.8).

Consequently, animal production is likely to be more sensitive to variations in sward conditions in high-performance than in low-performance animals. This association between level of production and herbage intake only applies between animals which have similar nutritional histories and in which the production difference reflects a difference in production potential. Where differences in animal performance are due to earlier differences in nutrition it is quite likely that previously underfed animals will have a higher herbage intake per unit of live weight (though not necessarily in absolute terms) despite a currently lower live weight or milk yield than others previously well fed. This difference in intake contributes to the often rapid recovery of body-weight or milk yield in animals whose food intake has previously been restricted.

The control of herbage intake

It is clear that herbage intake can be influenced by a number of sward and animal characteristics. Many of the individual effects have been described, but at present we lack the knowledge to predict with any certainty their combined effects on herbage intake.

Putting together the evidence discussed in this chapter, it is evident that the herbage intake of grazing animals is influenced by three principal factors:

1. The *feeding drive* which reflects the animal's current demand for nutrients, principally energy, and in particular the degree to which energy intake falls short of energy expenditure. Potential energy expenditure is a function of the size and stage of maturity of the animal, its productive state and genetic capability for production. However, its previous nutritional history will influence the level of production currently achievable and also the body reserves available to help to meet any established energy deficit.
2. The sensation of *physical satiety* which is a function of the de-

gree of distension of the alimentary tract, or of the abdomen, caused by the volume of digesta in the tract. The volume of digesta is a function of the amount of food eaten recently, its digestibility and the rates of digestion and of passage of undigested residues. The inherent capacities of the alimentary tract and the abdominal cavity reflect the size and maturity of the animal, modified by variations in the volume of the gravid uterus during pregnancy, or of abdominal fat stores.

3. *Behavioural constraints* which limit the potential rate of herbage consumption, and which may relate to both sward and

Figure 7.9   The control of herbage intake in grazing animals.

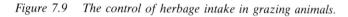
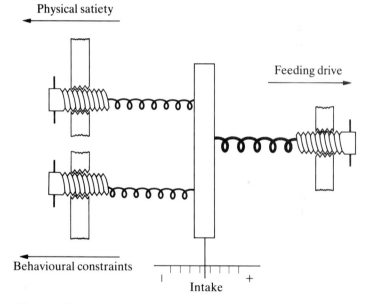

This is a diagrammatic representation of the links between the main factors influencing herbage intake in grazing animals. The right hand screw controls the feeding drive, serving to increase intake when the drive (tension on the spring) is increased and to reduce it when the drive diminishes. This effect is balanced by two counter-springs representing physical satiety and behavioural constraints respectively. Increasing these negative effects by increasing satiety and/or increasing the difficulty of grazing (increasing tension on the appropriate springs) will reduce intake, and vice versa. The intake achieved (position of the pointer) is the results of the balance struck between these three forces.

animal characteristics and their impact on intake per bite and bite rate. The structural characteristics of the sward are clearly of importance in this context, particularly sward height and density in so far as they influence intake per bite, and sward heterogeneity and its effect upon intake per bite or bite rate through selective grazing activity. The animal characteristics of primary importance are mouth size and the mobility of the jaw, lips and tongue, in terms of their influence on intake per bite, and detailed grazing strategy in so far as this affects both intake per bite and bite rate. All of these variables are influenced by the species and size of the animals concerned, and most of them may also reflect differences between animals in grazing experience.

The way in which these three forces are related is illustrated diagrammatically in Fig. 7.9, in which feeding drive is seen as a positive factor, and physical satiety and behavioural constraints as negative factors influencing intake. None of these factors is absolute, however. The level of herbage intake achieved in any particular circumstances will be determined by the balance struck between the three forces, rather than by any one limiting variable.

This concept of the control of herbage intake emphasizes the importance of the associative effects of a range of sward and animal characteristics, and the danger of concentrating on any single variable. It implies, for example, that an improvement in herbage digestibility will result in an increase in herbage intake only so long as it is not accompanied by adverse changes in sward height or herbage density. However, it should often be possible to decide which sward or animal variables are likely to be of primary importance in limiting intake in particular circumstances.

Chapter 8   Food conversion efficiency

Individual animals

The performance of individual animals improves progressively with increasing intake of a particular feed, though usually at a diminishing rate, up to the genetic limit of performance (Fig. 8.1). The efficiency of conversion of ingested nutrients into animal product $\left(\dfrac{\text{product}}{\text{food intake}}\right)$ increases at the same time, particularly in growing animals, because the proportion of the total nutrient intake required to maintain body function declines progressively as total intake increases. Animals with high production potential are therefore likely to have both a greater herbage intake and a higher food conversion efficiency than animals of lower potential in any given circumstances. Furthermore, the efficiency with which digested nutrients are used for maintenance or production will increase with increasing digestibility (or metabolizable nutrient concentration) in the diet, so that the higher the level of herbage intake and the greater the nutrient content of the herbage eaten, the greater the efficiency of conversion of ingested herbage into animal product is likely to be. However, the digestive efficiency of ruminant animals tends to decline as the amount of a particular food eaten increases, and there is also a progressive increase in the nutrient cost of successive increments of production (Fig. 8.1). These effects mean that food conversion efficiency cannot rise indefinitely, though ceiling efficiency is seldom approached in most of the conventional systems of ruminant animal production and there is usually a close relationship between nutrient intake and animal performance.

Animal populations

In meat-producing enterprises involving populations of animals with breeding females and, possibly, replacement females, the importance of production efficiency is even more heavily weighted because the maintenance demands of the breeding animals can make up a substantial proportion of the nutrient demands of the whole population. This means that the food conversion efficiency

Figure 8.1   The relationships between herbage intake, growth rate and efficiency of conversion of food into live weight gain in growing lambs.

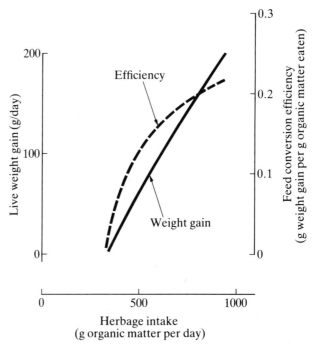

Both weight gain and the efficiency of conversion of food into animal product increase as herbage intake increases. The rate of improvement in efficiency declines rapidly at high levels of intake, but it would be unusual for efficiency to reach a ceiling in young growing animals on forage diets.

of the population as a whole will be directly related to the relative proportions of young animals intended for slaughter and of breeding stock, and will thus be directly affected by the breeding efficiency and prolificacy of the flock or herd (Fig. 8.2). This is particularly true where the life span of the growing animal is short and where its final weight, relative to that of breeding animals, is low.

Meat production enterprises involving breeding animals have a low efficiency (in biological terms) compared with meat production enterprises which do not carry the same direct costs of breeding animals, or systems of milk production (Table 8.1).

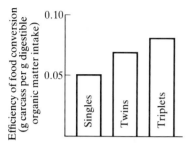

Figure 8.2 The influence of reproductive efficiency on food conversion efficiency of a flock of sheep.

The feed requirement of the ewe dominates the calculation of food conversion efficiency in breeding flocks. The extra food demands of prolific ewes and their lambs are small compared to the food requirements even of barren ewes, so the efficiency of food conversion (measured in this example as lamb carcass per unit of digestible organic matter consumed by the ewe and her lambs over the course of a year) increases rapidly as the reproductive rate increases. The substantially greater efficiency shown for weaned lambs in Fig. 8.1 is explained by the fact that they are no longer having to carry the food requirements of their dams.

Breeding females can introduce flexibility into management systems, however. This is because they can tolerate periods of sub-maintenance feeding without detriment to reproductive efficiency provided that the periods of underfeeding are not too serious or prolonged. This does not necessarily improve overall efficiency in biological terms, because a deficiency of nutrients at one stage of the production cycle must be made good at another if the enterprise is to survive. However, the attribute is particularly valuable in grassland enterprises where food supplies are likely to be highly seasonal.

Maximization of nutrient intake and food conversion efficiency is not necessarily the major objective of grazing management. Nevertheless there is often a strong argument for it in the case of young growing animals and lactating animals, the most respon-

*Table 8.1 Efficiency of conversion of food into animal product in alternative animal enterprises**

Enterprise	Efficiency
Dairy herd	0.21
Beef herd	0.07
Sheep flock	0.03
Beef finishing	0.15

* In this table efficiency is expressed as the amount of edible energy produced per unit of metabolizable energy consumed. The results for the dairy herd, beef herd and sheep flock take into account feed inputs to breeding females and to replacement stock, whereas for the beef-finishing enterprise they refer only to the growing animals themselves. Values for the dairy herd are based on a milk yield of 4100 kg/cow, for the beef herd on a 92% rearing rate of suckled calves, for the sheep flock on 150% lambs weaned, and for the beef-finishing enterprise on a growth rate of 1 kg/day.

sive classes of livestock with the most critical nutrient demands. In practical management systems this objective is constrained by the need to consider the needs of the different livestock classes on the farm and to ensure a sensible balance with the efficiencies of the other stages in the production process. Thus, in some cases it would be sound management policy to hold herbage intake and animal performance at submaximal levels by deliberately restricting sward conditions. Some of the implications of these issues are considered in Chapters 10 and 15.

Chapter 9

Sward conditions, herbage intake and animal performance

There will usually be a close relationship between the nutrient intake and performance of grazing animals. Thus, variations in sward conditions are likely to influence herbage intake and animal performance in a similar manner, and it is helpful to consider these effects together. Herbage intake and hence animal performance are sensitive to a range of sward characteristics (Ch. 7). Animals appear to respond primarily to variations in the amount and maturity of leaf material in the sward, and its distribution within the sward canopy. However, for practical purposes it will usually be necessary to derive simpler indices than this to guide grazing management decisions.

Under reasonably uniform conditions it is probably acceptable to reduce the complex of sward characteristics to two alternatives: **herbage mass** and **sward surface height**. Herbage mass is defined as the weight of herbage dry matter (DM) per unit ground area (usually expressed in kilograms per hectare) measured to ground level; sward surface height is the height of the top surface of the leaf canopy, measured on an undisturbed sward. Measurement procedures are explained in Chapter 18. These are the parameters for which most experimental information is available. Animals respond more consistently to variations in sward height than in herbage mass, and height is easily measured. In this chapter attention is concentrated principally upon the influence of sward height on both herbage intake and animal performance. Two important qualifications need to be borne in mind, however. The first relates to the strong influence of herbage digestibility upon intake and animal performance (Fig. 9.1); the effects of variations in sward height illustrated here relate specifically to swards maintained at a high level of digestibility. Second, the best information

Figure 9.1 The influence of herbage digestibility on calf growth.

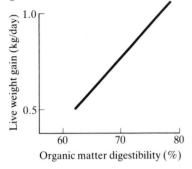

Live weight gain (kg/day)

Organic matter digestibility (%)

This illustrates how variations in the digestibility of the herbage eaten can affect the weight gain of growing calves. It is based on the relationship between herbage digestibility and herbage intake shown in Fig. 7.1.

available relates to comparatively simple swards under closely defined management conditions, and care is needed in attempting to extrapolate from one set of results to different circumstances. This point is exemplified by the need to quote separate results for swards managed in different ways.

The grazier must always be prepared to be flexible in striking a compromise between the needs of the sward and those of the animal population. Against this background it makes much more sense to think in terms of the way in which animal performance changes in response to changes in sward conditions than to define too rigidly the sward conditions 'required' to meet specified animal production objectives, though it is accepted that targets of one kind or another are a necessary part of the decision-making process.

Continuous stocking management

Under continuous stocking management, where animals are present on a sward for several weeks or months, herbage intake and animal performance increase at a progressively declining rate towards a maximum value as sward surface height increases (Fig. 9.2). The point at which intake or performance approaches the maximum can be defined as the critical height (point C in the figure). There is little value in providing sward conditions more generous than this, because further increases in height will not improve performance and will probably result in a reduction in grazing efficiency and, ultimately, in herbage production.

Point C is important in characterizing patterns of animal response, but it has been found to vary quite substantially in different experiments. This is probably due in part to simultaneous changes in other sward characteristics, particularly sward maturity, and in part to differences in the responses of different classes of animal. For example, increases in sward height are normally associated with increasing maturity and, hence, in a decline in the digestibility of the herbage eaten. This will itself tend to limit herbage intake as well as performance per unit of herbage eaten, thus offsetting some of the potential advantages of the in-

Figure 9.2   *The relationships between sward surface height and (a) herbage intake or (b) animal performance in grazing animals under continuous stocking management.*

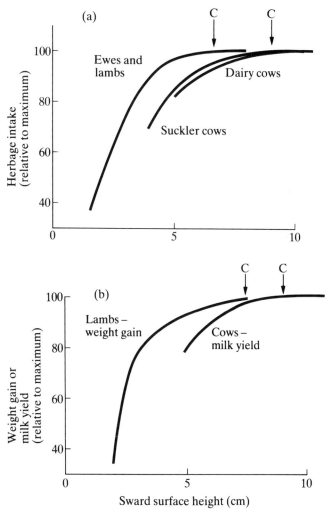

Intake and performance are expressed in relative terms, taking the maximum values as 100, in order to make comparison between animal classes easier. The intake responses of dairy cows and suckler cows are similar; intake starts to decline once sward height falls below 8–9 cm (point C). The intake of ewes and lambs (taken together) is maintained to lower levels of sward height, but starts to fall below 6–7 cm. Yield

per cow and growth per lamb follow roughly the same response curves as herbage intakes.

The dairy cows were spring-calving Friesians; beef cows were Hereford × Friesian to a Charolais bull; ewes were Greyface with single lambs to a Dorset Down ram.

creased height or mass. Therefore, herbage intake increases to greater sward heights where changes in digestibility are controlled than where they are not. This means that increase in height achieved by increasing fertilizer input to boost herbage growth rate is much more likely to result in improved animal performance than an increase in height achieved simply by allowing a sward to grow for a longer period of time before it is grazed.

It is also probable that a greater rate of herbage growth at any given height will itself serve to increase intake, simply because of the greater rate at which herbage grows into the surface layers of the sward. There are indications, too, that the critical point, C, is reached at lower heights on early spring swards than on established summer swards (Fig. 9.3). This effect may be due in part

Figure 9.3   The herbage intake of lactating ewes in spring and summer in relation to variations in sward height.

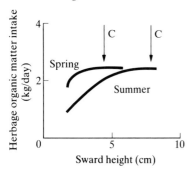

There is a marked disparity between the critical sward heights (C) on spring (May) swards and on summer (June – July) swards under continuous stocking management. The ewes in the spring study were in early lactation and nursing twins, whereas those in the summer study were in mid lactation and nursing singles, so intakes should not be compared in absolute terms. The important point is the horizontal displacement of the response lines. This effect is probably due to the generally lower tiller densities and greater leaf extension rates in spring than in summer swards.

The ewes were Greyface to a Dorset Down ram in each case. The swards were predominantly perennial ryegrass.

to the greater nutrient demands of lactation in early spring, but is also likely to be influenced by the generally lower tiller population densities and greater leaf extension rates in spring swards than on summer swards.

Cattle are probably more sensitive than sheep to declining sward height (Fig. 9.2), and there is some evidence that, on short swards, small animals are less severely limited than large animals of the same species. Within animal species, less productive groups

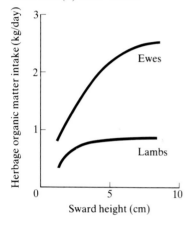

Figure 9.4 The influence of variations in sward height on the herbage intake of (a) lactating ewes and (b) their lambs.

These results relate to Greyface ewes with single lambs. The measurements were made in June and July when the lambs were 8–12 weeks old. The high milk yield of ewes grazing at the greater sward heights would restrict the herbage intake of their lambs.

of animals should be able to tolerate limiting sward conditions better than more productive animals. Also, the growth of suckling lambs or calves will be less sensitive than that of weaned animals because of the buffering effect of the dam's milk. The intake response of mother and young to variations in sward height may differ (Fig. 9.4) because the greater milk yield of a lactating animal on a relatively tall sward will itself tend to limit the herbage intake of her young.

Summarizing, under continuous stocking management, herbage intake and animal performance may be expected to start to decline when the surface height of the sward falls below 8–10 cm for grazing cattle and 6–7 cm for sheep (Table 9.1).

Table 9.1 Critical values of sward height required to maintain levels of herbage intake and animal performance close to maximum*

	C value (cm)
Continuous stocking	
Ewes and lambs:	
Spring	4–5
Summer	7–8
Beef cows and calves	9–10
Weaned calves	9–10
Dairy cows	9–10
Rotational grazing	
Ewes and lambs	6–7
Cows and calves	9–10
Weaned calves	11–12
Dairy cows	9–10

* The values shown in this table summarize the results of response studies of the kind shown in Figs 9.2–9.5. Note that the critical values quoted here relate specifically to animal performance, and take no account of effects on herbage production or utilization. The comparisons needed to reconcile sward and animal requirements are considered in Chapter 17.

Rotational grazing
management

Under rotational grazing management, in which animals return at intervals to the same area of sward and graze it down rapidly over a few hours or days, herbage intake and animal performance have often been related to variations in the daily allowance of herbage DM (kilograms per animal or per cent of animal weight

Figure 9.5   *The influence of post-grazing stubble height under rotational grazing management on (a) herbage intake and (b) animal performance.*

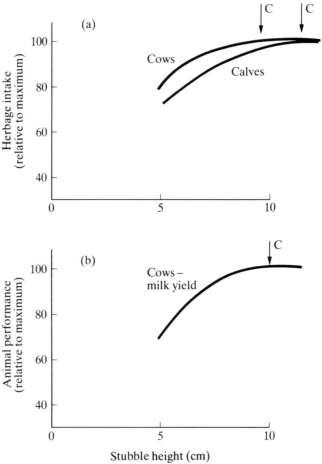

The critical post-grazing stubble heights shown are similar to the values shown for continuously stocked cattle swards in Fig. 9.2. Responses for sheep are not so well defined.

daily). The allowance is arrived at by dividing the number of animals per unit area into the herbage mass (weight of herbage DM per unit area of ground) and acts effectively as a rationing process. Herbage intake or animal performance increases at a declining rate with increasing allowance, usually reaching a plateau at a daily DM allowance equal to 10–12 per cent of the animal's body-weight for most classes of stock. Since this allowance is between two and three times the maximum daily herbage intake of the animals concerned, it inevitably involves a substantial wastage of herbage (see Ch. 10).

The response to varying herbage allowance tends to change with changing sward conditions, being steeper on tall or heavy swards than on short or light swards. This is because at equivalent allowances the area per animal is much smaller at high than at low herbage mass, so the rate at which the high mass sward is grazed down will be much greater. Also, a higher proportion of the herbage on a short sward is close to ground level and therefore relatively difficult to graze.

A description of the stubble remaining after grazing can also be used to assess the impact on animal performance under rotational grazing management. Again, the use of a single sward description is likely to involve over-simplification, but this is probably acceptable when used within the confines of a controlled rotational system with a relatively constant level of herbage mass or sward height before grazing. The critical post-grazing stubble height for cattle is approximately 10 cm (Fig. 9.5), but responses are not so well defined for sheep. Critical stubble heights under rotational management are similar to the critical surface heights for continuously stocked swards (Fig. 9.2).

The results illustrated in this chapter relate primarily to perennial ryegrass and ryegrass/white clover swards. There is little comparative information for alternative pasture species, though the relationships between herbage intake and either pasture height or herbage mass would be expected to change with variations in plant structure and morphology.

Chapter 10   Output from grazing systems

The ultimate output of animal product from a grazing system (quantity per unit area) is the result of the combined efficiencies of each of the steps in the production process. The efficiencies of the various stages were considered in isolation in earlier chapters, but grazing management is concerned with the interrelationships between the successive stages, and with the scope for controlling and manipulating overall efficiency.

Examples of the normal ranges of efficiency for each of the three main stages of production for temperate swards are given in Table 10.1. The energetic efficiency of each stage is used as a basis for comparison because energy provides a common thread throughout the production process and is a substantial component at each stage, but comparable tables can be constructed for other components. The efficiencies of the first step (the interception of the sun's energy and its conversion into plant tissue energy) and the last step (the conversion of ingested energy into animal product energy) are usually substantially lower than that of the intermediate step (the efficiency of ingestion or utilization of plant energy). However, the relative magnitude of the values shown is not as important in the present context as the scope for manipulating them and the extent to which they are interrelated. The principles governing these interrelationships and their ultimate outcome are the subject of this chapter, and involve a brief recapitulation of some of the evidence from Chapters 5, 7 and 8.

Herbage production and utilization

The efficiency of conversion of the sun's energy into plant tissue is always low, even when most of the incoming solar energy is intercepted by the sward canopy before it reaches the ground. This is due in part to the high energy demands of the photosynthetic process itself and the large amounts of energy expended in maintaining normal plant functions (Ch. 3), and in part to the

Table 10.1 The normal range of energetic efficiency for each of the three main stages of production in grassland enteprises on improved temperate swards*

Stage of production	Ratio	$\dfrac{\text{Energy output}}{\text{Energy input}}$
1. Herbage growth $= \dfrac{\text{Energy in herbage grown}}{\text{Energy in sunlight}}$		0.02–0.04
2. Herbage utilization $= \dfrac{\text{Energy in herbage consumed}}{\text{Energy in herbage grown}}$		0.4–0.8
3. Conversion to animal product $= \dfrac{\text{Energy in product}}{\text{Energy in herbage consumed}}$		0.02–0.05

* The energetic efficiency of herbage growth is a mean value for the whole year. Efficiency during the active growing season would be substantially higher: 0.04–0.08.

Values for the efficiency of conversion of the energy consumed into animal product refer to sheep flocks. They are based on the total herbage consumption of both ewes and lambs, and output in the form of lamb carcase. Examples for other animal enterprises are shown in Table 8.1.

Efficiency can vary by a factor of at least two at each stage. Note that efficiency in stages 1 and 3 is very much lower than in stage 2.

fact that in most temperate countries plant growth is limited by low temperatures for part of the year. Because of the enormous quantities of light energy reaching the earth, substantial improvements in plant growth should result from even modest improvements in the efficiency of the process, and there has always been great interest in the possibility of manipulating the sward to increase herbage production in a predictable fashion.

Both the rate of herbage production and the efficiency of use of incident light energy for growth can be substantially improved by increasing fertilizer inputs, particularly nitrogen, and, in some cases, by correcting soil pH and improving drainage. The results shown in Chapter 5 also demonstrate the influence of sward conditions on the efficiency of herbage production, growth rates increasing to a sward surface height of at least 5–6 cm, equivalent to a leaf area index (LAI) of 3.0–4.0. However, as a consequence of the balance between the rates of growth and senescence at greater levels of sward height and LAI, the rate of net herbage production changes to a very limited extent over a substantial range of sward conditions (see Fig. 5.5).

There is a generally inverse relationship between efficiencies in the first two phases of the production process, the combined effect being dominated by low growth efficiency on hard grazed swards and by low utilization efficiency on laxly grazed swards (Fig. 10.1). Managements which maximize net herbage production per unit area therefore depend upon avoiding treatments

Figure 10.1   *The influence of sward height maintained under continuous stocking management upon the efficiencies of herbage growth and utilization.*

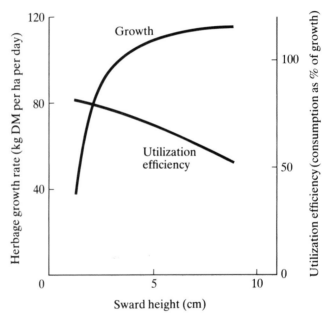

The rate of herbage growth (and therefore the efficiency of conversion of incident light energy into plant energy) increases by a factor of three over the range of sward surface height from 1.5 to 5.0 cm (Fig. 5.5), but changes little at greater heights. The efficiency of utilization of the herbage grown $\left(= \dfrac{consumption}{growth} \right)$, *on the other hand, falls progressively over this range of herbage mass from a maximum of about 80 per cent.*

$$\textit{Net herbage production} = \textit{Growth} \times \frac{\textit{utilization efficiency}}{100}$$

severe enough to depress herbage growth seriously at one end of the range, and those lax enough to result in excessive losses at the other. However, the substantial zone of approximate balance between the rates of growth and senescence (see Fig. 5.5) indicates the scope for manipulating sward conditions to the benefit of the animal population without adversely affecting net herbage production.

Herbage consumption and animal performance

Herbage consumption per unit area is the product of intake per animal and the number of animals per unit area. Herbage consumption per unit area equates with net herbage production in Fig. 5.5 and determines the efficiency of herbage utilization. A high rate of consumption per unit area should therefore be a desirable objective, but this introduces the second example of a conflict between efficiencies in different phases of the production process.

The efficiency of conversion of ingested herbage into animal product increases progressively as intake per animal increases. The efficiency of herbage utilization, on the other hand, increases as herbage consumption per unit area increases. Herbage intake per animal and consumption per unit area are inversely related, at least up to levels of herbage utilization beyond which herbage growth rates are depressed, and this means that the efficiencies of the processes of utilization and conversion are also likely to be inversely related.

This is principally a reflection of the effect of distributing a limited amount of food among different populations of animals; where all the food is being consumed, more animals mean less food per animal and therefore lower individual performance. Under grazing conditions, however, the story is more complex for several reasons. It is not sensible to think in terms of a fixed food supply because grazing animals seldom, if ever, eat all of the herbage on a sward even when they are extremely hungry. Furthermore, the proportion of the herbage allocated which is actually eaten falls progressively as the amount allocated (and the amount eaten) increases. This point is illustrated in Fig. 10.2, which relates to rotational grazing management. In these circumstances there is a close, negative relationship between the proportion of the daily allowance which is eaten and intake per animal. In addition, the consequences of the original treatments mean that there are likely to be progressive changes with time in

Figure 10.2 *The relationships between daily herbage allowance under rotational grazing management, herbage intake per animal and the efficiency of herbage utilization.*

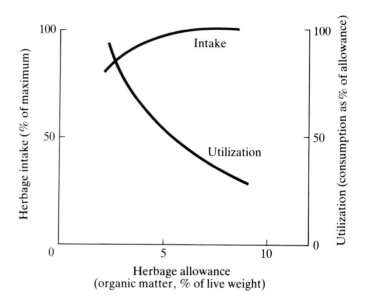

Under rotational grazing management, herbage intake only reaches a maximum when the daily allowance of herbage is equal to at least twice the amount eaten. The efficiency of herbage utilization falls progressively as herbage allowance increases, so there is an inverse relationship between herbage intake per animal and utilization efficiency (derived from information given in Fig. 9.5)

It should be noted that the expression of herbage utilization used here is not the same as that defined in Chapter 5 and Fig. 10.1, which relates to the balance between herbage consumption and herbage growth. Calculating utilization efficiency as $\left(\dfrac{consumption}{allowance}\right)$ can substantially underestimate true efficiency $\left(\dfrac{consumption}{growth}\right)$, because of the uneaten herbage which is carried over from one grazing to the next and which may, in effect, be counted several times. It is easier to measure herbage mass at a point in time than to try to estimate the rate of growth of herbage over time, so utilization efficiency is commonly expressed as $\left(\dfrac{consumption}{allowances}\right)$ but it is as well to bear in mind the implications of using this expression.

the amount of herbage per animal, uneaten herbage accumulating at high allowances, but the sward being grazed down progressively at low allowance.

Stocking rate

So far the associations between sward and animal have been described in terms of a series of static 'snapshots': of the effects of sward height on rates of herbage growth and senescence and on intake per animal, for example, or the effects of herbage allowance on utilization efficiency. But grazing systems are dynamic entities and can be strongly affected by the progressive development of plant and animal responses over time. In this respect the link between the sward and animal components of grazing systems is the **stocking rate** – the number of animals per unit area for a substantial period of time, often, but not necessarily, one grazing season. Stocking rate has its limitations as an index of measurement because it does not take into account the productive potential of the sward or the potential herbage intake of a population of animals. The term is widely used and provides a convenient basis for considering the cumulative effects of the steps in the production process. However, it needs to be emphasized that the effects of stocking rate on herbage production and animal performance shown in this chapter illustrate generalized relationships and do not provide an acceptable basis for management decisions in specific cases (see Chs 15–19).

Increases in stocking rate will increase the severity and, under continuous stocking management, the frequency of defoliation of individual tillers in the sward. These effects are likely to be reinforced by a greater degree of treading damage and soil compaction at high stocking rate, but may be offset by the more effective recycling of plant nutrients in dung and urine. An increase in stocking rate will also reduce the area of rejected herbage round dung pats.

The influence of stocking rate upon tissue turnover in the sward is illustrated in Fig. 10.3. This demonstrates in a slightly different form the point made in Chapter 5 that wide variations in grazing management apparently have little effect upon net herbage production. The rate of herbage growth is depressed at high stocking rate, but the major effect is upon the efficiency of utilization of the herbage grown.

Under continuous stocking management, sward height at the time of grazing will be negatively related to stocking rate. This is

Figure 10.3 The influence of stocking rate on rates of herbage growth, senescence and net production.

Here the information from Fig. 5.5 is plotted in a different way. The rate of herbage growth increases as stocking rate is reduced, but this effect is eventually offset by increasing losses to senescence so that net herbage production reaches a plateau and eventually starts to decline again at low stocking rate.

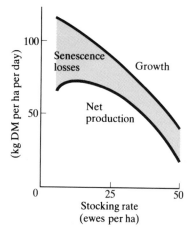

because of the combined effects of less efficient utilization and greater intake per animal under laxer grazing. The relationship is illustrated in Fig. 10.4. At the same time, the decline in grazing efficiency at lower stocking rates will result in a decline in the proportion of green leaf as stem and senescent material accumulate (Fig. 10.5). The effect upon the digestibility of the herbage eaten depends upon the opportunity for animals to select live material. Usually the effect is greatest on extensive grazings where uneaten herbage may accumulate over several seasons and interfere with access to fresh growth. On swards under relatively intensive management the digestibility of the diet is often lower in animals grazing at high stocking rate because of the limited amount of green herbage in the sward (Fig. 10.5).

Figure 10.4 The relationship between sward height and stocking rate under continuous stocking management.

This illustrates the relationship between the levels of surface height on continuously stocked swards and the stocking rate needed to maintain them. Stocking rate falls rapidly as surface height increases, tending to settle out at a low level.

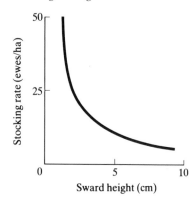

Herbage intake per animal and, in growing animals at least, individual animal performance decline progressively as stocking rate increases (Fig. 10.6). The indications are that this is true even down to very low stocking rates over the course of a grazing season. This suggests that intake is ultimately more sensitive to declining herbage mass than to declining herbage quality, but in any case the stocking rate at which low quality is an important consideration should be below the range of practical interest. The pattern of response in animal performance over a range of stocking rates changes with time (Fig. 10.7); the simple linear response measured over a full season is a reflection of the fact that animals at lower stocking rates tend to grow faster for longer than animals at higher stocking rates.

The relationship between stocking rate and individual performance in lactating animals, and particularly in ewe/lamb and

Figure 10.5 *The influence of stocking rate upon (a) sward morphology and (b) digestibility of the herbage eaten.*

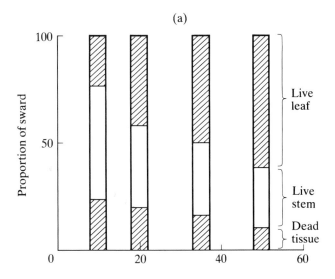

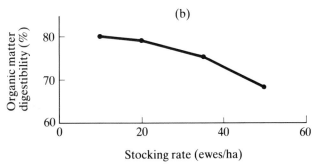

The low efficiency of herbage utilization at low stocking rate results in the accumulation of substantial amounts of stem and dead tissue and a marked reduction in the proportion of live leaf in the sward, but not necessarily in the herbage eaten. High stocking rates ensure the maintenance of a high proportion of leaf, but may nevertheless result in a depression in the digestibility of the herbage eaten because they result in a short, dense sward which reduces the opportunity for selective grazing.

Figure 10.6   *The relationship between stocking rate and (a) individual animal performance or (b) animal production per unit area over a grazing season.*

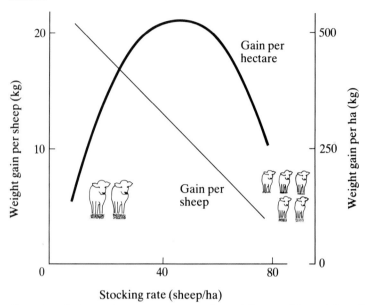

Stocking rate (sheep/ha)

Over the whole grazing season, or a substantial part of it, weight gain per animal declines progressively with increasing stocking rate. These are results of an experiment with growing sheep, but the result would be very similar with cattle. Output per hectare (weight gain per animal × number of animals per hectare) falls away at the same rate on both sides of the stocking rate giving maximum output per hectare – in this case at about 45 growing sheep per hectare. Low output (left) is the result of low herbage utilization efficiency because of low stocking rate; low output (right) is a consequence of low feed conversion efficiency because of poor individual performance. The relationship is not so clear-cut in dairy cows or in cow/calf and ewe/lamb enterprises, because use of body reserves by the lactating female can help to buffer the effects of increasing stocking rate.

cow/calf systems, is more complicated because of the ability of the dam to make use of body reserves to sustain lactation where herbage intake is limiting. On a year-by-year basis this distinction may not be particularly important because of the need to replenish at one stage of the production cycle the reserves lost at another if performance is not to be progressively depressed. The

Figure 10.7   *Changes with time in the relationship between stocking rate and individual animal performance.*

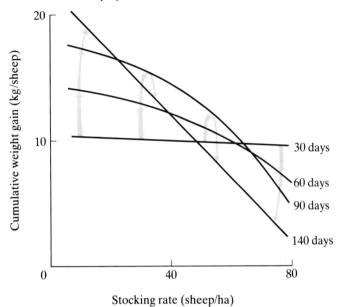

The relationship between stocking rate and cumulative animal gain changes over the season. Here is an illustration of the developing pattern leading to the final relationship shown in Fig. 10.6. For an initial period animals gained weight at a similar rate at all stocking rates, but as the initial herbage reserves were used up the animals at high stocking rate started to lose weight. As the season progressed animals reached a peak weight at progressively lower stocking rate, and eventually weight increase was sustained only at the lowest stocking rates.

In normal circumstances it would not often be sensible to maintain stocking rates resulting in substantial weight loss, particularly in growing animals. However, this is a very good illustration of the progressive changes in the balance between sward and animal.

importance of this consideration will depend in part upon the patterns of seasonal variation in herbage production and demands. In production systems with breeding animals the sensitivity of reproduction in the dam to variations in stocking rate is likely to be lower than that of performance in the offspring.

The relationship between stocking rate and output per unit area (individual performance × stocking rate) takes the form shown in Fig. 10.6. Output per unit area declines at low stocking rates because of low animal numbers and at high stocking rates because of low production per animal, but changes are relatively slow about the stocking rate which maximizes output per unit area.

It is often said that the grazier's main problem is to achieve a reasonable compromise between a stocking rate which results in high performance per individual animal and one which gives high output per unit area. The point is a perfectly reasonable one to make, though a directly analogous question can be posed (but seldom is) about the allocation of a given supply of stored food to different numbers of animals. The compromise solution is not easy to achieve in production systems where animal performance declines steadily with increasing stocking rate, as in Fig. 10.6, because in these circumstances it is not often sensible to fix stocking rate close to the point maximizing animal performance. The market provides an answer to the question in systems of meat production because it is usually possible to define a minimum acceptable carcass weight, and this sets a lower limit to individual animal performance against which to pitch stocking rate. Answers to these questions require information on product values and production costs.

Generally speaking, the stocking rate which maximizes the product value per unit area from meat-producing enterprises will be lower than the stocking rate which maximizes physical output. This is because the value per unit of product tends to fall with declining weight gain and product size, but the outcome is heavily dependent upon marketing strategy. For milk-producing or wool-producing enterprises unit values are unlikely to be much influenced by stocking rate so that differences between the stocking rates maximizing output in physical and financial terms will be small.

The fixed and variable costs per unit area are also likely to rise sharply with increasing stocking rate however. Fixed costs are linked to the number of animals required and any provisions for housing them; variable costs may be affected by the need for more supplementary feed and medicaments at high stocking rate. Thus the margin over variable costs and, particularly, the margin over variable and fixed costs are likely to be maximized for any livestock enterprise at stocking rates a good deal lower than that at which output per unit area is maximized.

Chapter 11 **Plants**

Choice of plant species and cultivars

Swards for grazing animals range from the ultra-simple all-grass swards which may, in extreme cases, contain only one grass variety, to the highly complex permanent pastures which frequently contain more than ten species of grass and twice as many species of broad-leaved plants. The botanical composition of long-established grassland is very much a product of the combined influences of soil, climate and management, including both grazing or cutting practices and fertilizer use.

There has been much controversy in recent years about the advantages to be gained from replacing an existing, established sward with new plant varieties, and about the basis for choice between alternative varieties. In many circumstances grazing management and fertilizer inputs are likely to have a much greater influence on herbage production than does plant genotype. Also, within limits, a high population of leafy tillers and a good ground cover are more important in determining the performance of a sward than is the genetic make-up of the plants of which it is composed. Furthermore, the high tiller population of well-managed old grassland is much less vulnerable to damage than the relatively low tiller population in an establishing sward. Thus, the decision to change an established sward should not be taken lightly, and there is often little point in changing the plants without changing management at the same time. Nevertheless, when a sward has to be sown it is important to make an informed choice among the plant material available. Choice will be strongly influenced by the productive potential and nutritive value of the plant species and cultivars available. However, particularly in the more extreme climates, tolerance of winter cold or summer drought and resistance to pests and diseases are likely to be of equal or greater importance.

In most countries essential information on the productive potential of the alternative grass species and varieties is provided by national agencies. This information can often be augmented by detailed recommendations for local conditions. The information is usually based largely on the results of cutting trials, and sound comparative evidence on the response of different plant genotypes to grazing is seldom available. Supplementary evidence from measurements of production under grazing conditions, and associated information on levels of animal performance, will be particularly useful when it can be obtained. Claims about the 'palatability' or 'acceptability' of particular varieties are of doubtful value in the absence of this kind of information.

The comparative yields of representative cultivars of the major grass species in the UK are listed in Table 11.1. The yields quoted here were measured under a frequent cutting management with a high input of fertilizer nitrogen (N), and are probably the best indication available of production potential (at least in relative terms) under grazing conditions. Clearly the differences in total

Table 11.1   Comparative yields of representative cultivars of the main grass species under standard cutting managements*

Species	Yield (kg DM per ha)
Perennial ryegrass (*Lolium perenne*)	10 800
Italian ryegrass (*L. multiflorum*)	10 800
Meadow fescue (*Festuca pratensis*)	10 000
Timothy (*Phleum pratense*)	9 600
Cocksfoot (*Dactylis glomerata*)	10 000
Tall fescue (*F. arundinacea*)	10 700

* These results refer to grasses grown singly in small plots at each of four centres in the UK. The measurements were made in the first year after sowing, on plots receiving 340 kg of N per ha and cut nine times at monthly intervals. Under this management the differences between species were relatively small. Only two cultivars per species contributed to this comparison, but results from other sources indicate that the general comparisons are reasonable.

annual yield of herbage between the main cultivated grass species are small. Differences are greater under a system of infrequent cutting, when yields are highest for Italian ryegrass and tall fescue, but this kind of management is hardly relevant to grazing conditions.

In the case of plants to be used in grazed swards, uniformity of production, high nutritive value, flexibility of use and tolerance of management variation are also characteristics of major importance. Perennial ryegrass is the grass of choice on all of these counts in areas with a reasonable rainfall distribution and without extreme winter temperatures. It is a species which normally maintains a high tiller population and is better adapted to grazing than to cutting management. Grasses like timothy and meadow fescue are also tolerant of a range of grazing conditions and are often sold in seeds mixtures with perennial ryegrass. Timothy has a relatively high cold tolerance and cocksfoot a relatively high tolerance of dry conditions. There is little evidence to suggest that mixtures of species are any better or any worse than perennial ryegrass alone under comparable grazing managements, and no real indication that mixtures provide greater management flexibility.

Differences in the seasonal patterns of herbage production are of potential value. Figure 11.1 shows the seasonal production curves of representative cultivars of three different grass species to illustrate the potential range of variation available. On the face of it the variation between species in early growth seems to be relatively small, and differences between cultivars within a species may be almost as great as the variation between species (Fig. 11.2). However, differences of only a week or two in the acceleration of growth in the spring can be of critical importance in many grassland enterprises. Spring growth potential is illustrated in a different way in Fig. 11.3. Italian ryegrass and tall fescue are generally recognized to have better early growth than most other species. There is no comparable information for grazed swards.

The curves shown in Fig. 11.1 and 11.2 were measured under limited irrigation and, even under these conditions, production from timothy fell to a low level in mid season. In the absence of irrigation the mid-season production from most other species would also be depressed in a dry year.

Species like Italian ryegrass, tall fescue and cocksfoot with

Figure 11.1   Seasonal patterns of herbage production in three grass species: (——) S170 tall fescue; (— — —) S23 perennial ryegrass; (—·—·) S48 timothy. From Anslow, R. C. and Green, J. O. (1967) The seasonal growth of pasture grasses. J. Agric. Sci., Camb., 68, 109–22.

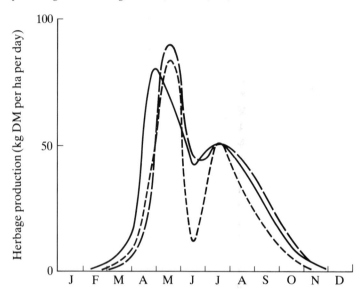

These production curves are derived from grass plots cut every 3–4 weeks, receiving over 300 kg of N per hectare in frequent small applications, and with irrigation to limit water stress on the plant.

The curves for individual cultivars within a species can differ quite substantially (see Fig. 11.2) and it is not possible to choose a 'representative' cultivar for a species. Thus, although the curves shown are indicative of differences between species their main purpose is to show the range of variation available.

Seasonal variations in herbage production under continuous stocking management are substantially smaller than those shown here and in Fig. 11.2, though variations under rotational grazing may be similar to those under cutting management.

special growth attributes can make substantial contributions to grassland enterprises as special-purpose swards in particular circumstances. However, they cannot easily be incorporated into general-purpose swards and their use can limit flexibility for the whole grassland area. All three species require close control of grazing to maintain nutritive value, and cocksfoot and tall fescue in particular tend rapidly to become dominant in mixed swards

Figure 11.2 *Seasonal patterns of herbage production in two cultivars of perennial ryegrass with contrasting heading dates: (──) S23, (‑‑‑‑) S24. From Anslow, R. C. and Green, J. O. (1967) The seasonal growth of pasture grasses. J. Agric. Sci., Camb., 68, 109–22.*

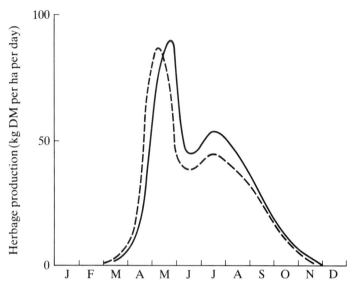

These production curves, relating to two long-established cultivars of perennial ryegrass, indicate the range of variation within the species in earliness of growth and earliness of attaining peak growth. In the perennial ryegrasses there is a close correlation between the earliness of growth and the heading date (the date on which 50 per cent of the seed heads have emerged), the spring peak of growth coinciding with ear formation. The associated changes in the digestibility of herbage are shown in Fig. 11.3.

because of their aggressive growth and because animals prefer to graze other species.

Perennial ryegrass has relatively high requirements for soil pH and mineral nutrients if it is to sustain high levels of production. Grass species which have been advocated for limiting conditions of soil and climate with low fertilizer inputs include red fescue (*Festuca rubra*) and Yorkshire fog (*Holcus lanatus*). These species may have a place in difficult environments but they are generally of lower digestibility than perennial ryegrass and have a poorer compatibility with white clover.

Figure 11.3   *Herbage accumulation and the decline in digestibility during spring growth in five grass species: (1) Italian ryegrass; (2) early perennial ryegrass; (3) late perennial ryegrass; (4) tall fescue; (5) cocksfoot. From Green, J. O., Corrall, A. J. and Terry, R. A. (1971) Grass species and varieties. Relationships between stage of growth, yield and forage quality. Technical Report No. 8, Grassland Research Institute.*

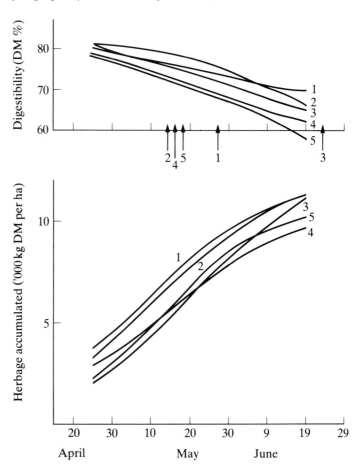

These results refer to plots of representative varieties of five grass species allowed to grow undisturbed until mid June with a nitrogen input of 175 kg/ha, sample areas being cut at 7–10-day intervals to measure herbage accumulation. The arrows indicate the dates of 50 per cent ear emergence for the five varieties listed. Again the differences between species appear to be relatively small, but in fact

*there is almost a twofold difference in the accumulated herbage mass
in late April and early May.*

*The decline in herbage digestibility with increasing maturity is also
shown. Note that there is no particular correlation, across species,
between early production and digestibility, but cocksfoot and tall
fescue are relatively low in digestibility throughout. Digestibility
differences are small but important initially, and increase progressively
with time.*

Many varieties of perennial ryegrass are available which differ
primarily in the earliness of growing and heading (Fig. 11.2), and
in growth habit. Early growing varieties may be of advantage in
enterprises where early grazing is important – in grassland sheep
flocks or spring-calving dairy herds for example – but early
growth is often associated with early heading and reduced summer growth or nutritive value. The later-heading varieties tend to
start growth later but to maintain more uniform growth
throughout the summer, and have been shown to sustain better
animal production over the season in grassland beef systems.
Generally the more prostrate varieties are designated as most
suitable for grazing and the more erect varieties for conservation.
However, the evidence discussed in Chapter 7 suggests that, other
things being equal, an erect growth habit is likely to encourage
high herbage intake. Virtually all of the perennial ryegrasses will
readily adapt their growth habit to suit a particular management
and the choice is probably not critical. Some of the tetraploid
ryegrasses have been shown to have higher intake potential than
the normal diploid varieties in indoor trials (tetraploid varieties
carry twice as many chromosomes as diploid varieties), and they
also have a more erect growth habit and larger tillers which improve herbage intake under grazing conditions. Improved levels
of animal performance have also been claimed for them on a farm
scale, but their ability to meet the requirements for general-purpose grazed swards is not yet clear.

It is usual to include more than one perennial ryegrass variety
in a seeds mixture for grazing, the assumption being that this will
improve the uniformity of herbage production and nutritive
value. It is difficult to demonstrate any real advantage from this
practice but there is unlikely to be any disadvantage either unless
management and utilization are to be highly specialized.

There is more controversy about the place of the legume in

grazed swards, most of it concerned with the value of white clover (*Trifolium repens*) since this is the only legume currently available which is flexible enough to consider for general-purpose grazed swards. The other major legumes, red clover (*T. pratense*) and lucerne (*Medicago sativa*) have their place as special-purpose crops, principally in drier areas, but have very specific management requirements. *Lotus* spp. (*L. corniculatus* and *L. pedunculatus*) are of increasing interest for soils of low fertility.

In the UK, estimates from plots of white clover cut less frequently than the grass plots referred to in Table 11.1 give an annual yield of about 7000 kg of dry matter per hectare. The yield of clover growing in association with grass is usually substantially less than this, though the N fixed from the atmosphere by the clover plant makes a substantial contribution to the growth of the companion grass. The N responses of grass and grass/clover swards are considered in Chapter 12. Furthermore, the presence of clover may improve the intake and nutritive value of a grass diet, thus enhancing animal performance. Clover is slower to grow in the spring than grass but maintains growth better during the summer. However, because of its sensitivity to shading and its susceptibility to fungal and insect pests, its growth and its N contribution can be erratic. For these reasons its use in European intensive grassland systems has not been favoured, reliance being placed on fertilizer N for all herbage production. In New Zealand, with more favourable climatic condition for growth, white clover is an essential component of most pastures.

Much research needs to be done to define desirable levels of clover in mixed swards and the most reliable procedures for establishing and maintaining these levels. In the meantime, however, there is no good reason not to include clover seed in a mixture at the rate of about 10 per cent of the total by weight, even in swards which are likely to receive high inputs of N fertilizer. Most of the grazing strategies discussed in Chapter 17 are likely to minimize the competition for light which can inhibit clover production in mixed swards.

The available white clover varieties are normally characterized on the basis of leaf and petiole size. The smaller-leaved, more prostrate varieties may be more resistant to grazing and the larger-leaved varieties better able to withstand shading effects in tall swards. However, most clover varieties adapt quickly to variations in sward management. Recommended varieties of white clover are also set out in the national lists.

Sward establishment

The major requirements for sward establishment are preliminary attention to drainage, to the pH of the soil and the status of the major and minor plant nutrients and the preparation of a firm seed bed. In recent years there has been rapid development of minimum cultivation techniques–surface seeding or direct drilling. Initial lime and fertilizer applications should be based on preliminary soil analyses. Early applicarion of fertilizer N helps to stimulate seedling growth. Rapid tillering is encouraged by the early initiation and subsequent maintenance of grazing.

Careful grazing management is essential during the establishment phase in order to encourage tillering in grasses and stolon development in cloves. Continuous stocking to maintain a sward height of 6–8 cm is probably a reasonable target. If intermittent grazing is preferred it should occur at intervals of no more than 3 weeks and involve grazing down to no less than 5 cm. Grazing by sheep is less damaging than grazing by cattle in the early stages of development.

Grazing and sward composition

Variations in grazing management can have substantial effects on the structure and botanical composition of swards. These effects are usually more obvious where the opportunity for selective grazing is great than where it is not, but there is scope for manipulating sward composition even under uniform defoliation.

Continuous hard grazing will maintain a short, prostrate sward and will increase the proportion of plant species and varieties with a prostrate growth habit at the expense of those with a more erect habit of growth. Lax or intermittent grazing will have the opposite effect. Many grass species, particularly the perennial ryegrasses, show very considerable phenotypic plasticity so that a single-species sward can assume widely different growth habit and structure depending upon management.

Variation in growth habit can influence the contribution of individual plant species to the diet of the grazing animal, and the impact of defoliation on individual species, even when a sward is defoliated very uniformly. Two examples will illustrate the point.

(a) **Grass/legume balance.** It was suggested in Chapter 4 that the ratio of clover to grass in the herbage consumed by sheep on a mixed sward may, often, simply reflect the species balance in the surface layers of the sward within which the animals are grazing. However, because the clover plant places a higher proportion of its leaf in the upper layers of the sward than the grass plant does, the consequence is that even a completely non-selective grazing will result in a more complete defoliation of the clover than of the grass. Thus the efficiency of utilization (*consumption/growth*) will be greater for clover than for grass (Table 11.2) simply as a consequence of their different growth habits, and this will put the clover at a competitive disadvantage quite independent of any implications of preferential grazing. This is the situation in continuously stocked and relatively short swards. In taller swards most clover varieties are likely to be overtopped by companion grasses and in these circumstances clover growth will be inhibited by competition for light. Thus, the clover content of a sward is likely to be reduced by both hard and lax grazing.

(b) Competition between perennial ryegrass and weed grasses.
Annual meadow grass (*Poa annua*) is a low-growing grass which can readily colonize grassland because of the rapid development of reproductive tillers at most seasons of the year and a rapid development of new plants from seed. It can have a substantial presence in many swards but, because its leaves tend to be overtopped by the leaves of the sown grass with which it is associated, it makes a relatively small contribution to herbage consumption (Table 11.2). Managements which maintain a high tiller population and a complete leaf cover will limit the ingress of invader

Table 11.2 The growth and efficiency of utilization of perennial ryegrass, annual meadow grass and white clover in mixed swards

	Perennial ryegrass	Annual meadow grass	White clover
		(kg DM per ha per day)	
Growth rate	54	20	3.5
Consumption rate	37	11	3.1
Senescence rate	17	9	0.4
Utilization efficiency $= \dfrac{\text{Consumption}}{\text{Growth}}$	0.69	0.55	0.89

plants, including *Poa*, but sites of sward damage will always provide access for these species.

The additional effects of selective grazing on the species balance of intensively grazed grassland are likely to be small, except in the case of the ingress of weed species like nettle, rushes and docks which are usually avoided by sheep and cattle. Selection is strongly influenced by the contrast between the components of the sward. It will therefore be greatest in under-utilized swards, and in natural swards, where the contrasts are greatest. In addition, many of the plant species in native grassland are more sensitive to the effects of selective defoliation than cultivated species are. There is little to be gained by drawing up detailed lists of preferences but, for example, the preferences of animals for white clover, the ryegrasses, timothy and meadow fescue in comparison with cocksfoot and tall fescue at equivalent stages of growth are well recognized. Plant species low in the preference list cannot easily be controlled without hard grazing.

The conclusion may be drawn that management is likely to have a greater influence upon herbage and animal production than does the choice of plant genotype. This is only true up to a point, however. It would be reasonable to argue that the use of improved varieties is unlikely to make up for management deficiencies and, conversely, that efficient management should reduce the need for sward replacement and hence the opportunity to try out new plant material. However, where sward replacement is necessary there should still be advantages to be gained from the judicious choice of plant varieties to suit the requirements of particular enterprises, provided that the choice can be made on the basis of appropriate evidence.

Chapter 12 Soils and fertilizers

Plant growth is dependent upon a continuing supply of mineral nutrients from the soil. All nutrients must be in solution in the soil water before they can be absorbed by plant roots but, once absorbed, the minerals may be built into the structure of the plant or retained in a soluble form in the cell contents. The minerals in plant material eaten by grazing animals may be digested and absorbed from the alimentary tract, or pass out undigested in faeces. Substantial quantities of the minerals absorbed are eventually excreted in the urine, but in each case a proportion is retained in animal tissue or secreted in milk. Thus, each of the minerals is involved in a cyclic movement from soil to plant, plant to animal and back to the soil. Figures 12.1 and 12.2 illustrate diagrammatically the cyclic movements of three major plant nutrients, nitrogen (N), phosphorus (P) and potassium (K), in grazing systems.

Each cycle is augmented by the release of minerals in soluble form from the weathering and breakdown of soil particles and from mineral fertilizers added to the soil, and by small amounts of solid or soluble material from the atmosphere. The fixation of N from the air by bacteria growing in nodules on the roots of leguminous plants can make an important additional contribution to the N cycle (Fig. 2.2) Soluble minerals may be lost by leaching or surface runoff, and N may also be lost as a consequence of the evaporation of ammonia from the soil surface, principally from urine patches.

Soil conditions

Although virtually all soils contain large quantities of all three minerals, most of these reserves are in an insoluble form and the output from a grazing system is determined largely by the rate at which minerals move round the cycle. The rate of uptake of each mineral is effectively limited by the rate at which it passes into solution, and rates of release of soluble constituents from both the inorganic and organic fractions of the soil can be very low.

Figure 12.1   The sources of P and K and their movements in grazing systems.

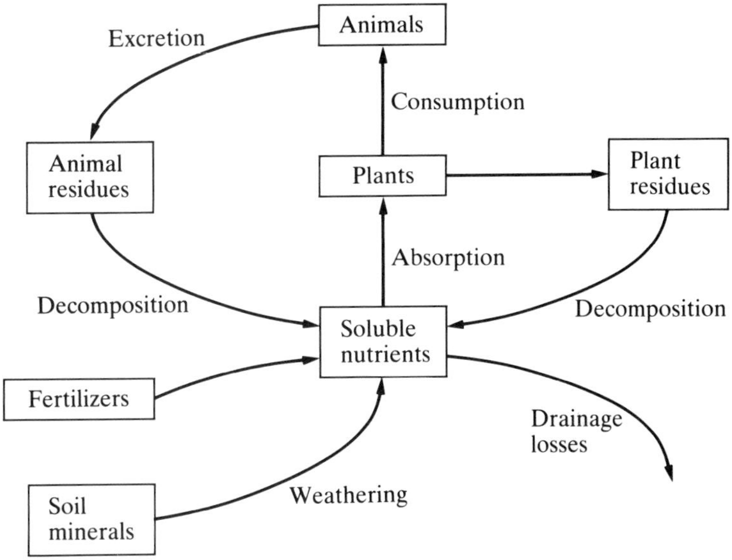

*Plant nutrients are released by the weathering of soil minerals and are
introduced in mineral fertilizers and organic manures. Small quantities
may also be derived from atmospheric pollutants or surface water. The
plant can only make use of these in a soluble form. Nutrients can be
recycled in grazing systems in the form of uneaten plant residues or as
animal excreta. The nutrients in urine are readily available to the
plant. Those in faeces or in plant material only become available when
released as a result of the decomposition of the organic residues.
Animal residues are broken down more readily than plant residues, so
the efficiency of the recycling process increases as the proportion of
the plant material eaten (utilization efficiency) increases. Soluble
nutrients which are not taken up by plants may be lost in drainage
water. This diagram of nutrient supply and movement within a
grazing system is appropriate for the major nutrients P and K. The
cycle for N is shown in Fig 12.2.*

Examples are given in Table 12.1. Though the amounts of plant
nutrients added in conventional fertilizers are small in comparison
to the total soil pool, they are relatively easily soluble and therefore make a disproportionately large contribution to output.

The nature of the soil influences herbage production through
its effect on the supply of soluble nutrients, which is much greater

Figure 12.2   Sources and movements of N in grazing systems.

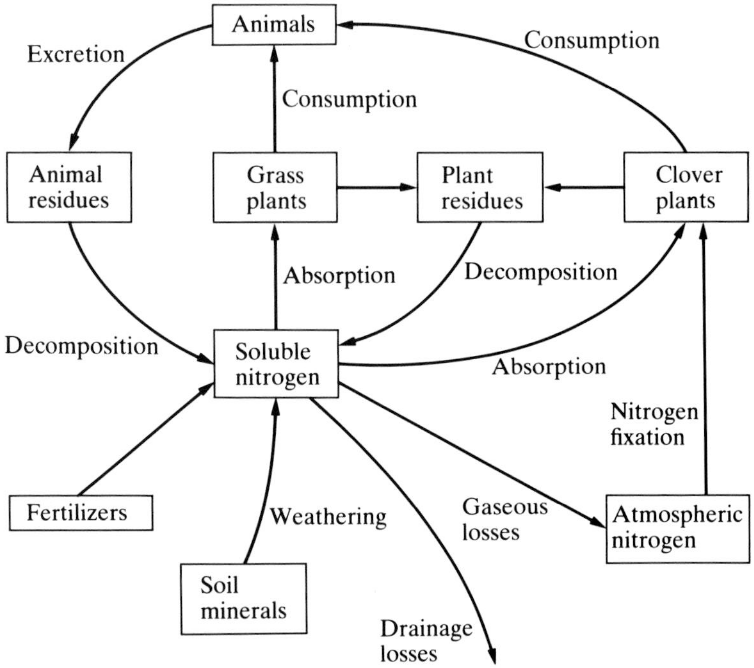

The middle and left-hand sectors here are similar to Fig. 12.1, but the clover plant provides an important extra source of N through the ability of the symbiotic rhizobium bacteria growing in root nodules to fix N from the atmosphere in a form readily available to the plant. To be of use to the associated grass plants the clover foliage must first pass through the cycle of consumption–excretion–decomposition, or clover roots and nodules, and ungrazed foliage, must themselves decompose. Nitrogen may also return to the atmosphere in the form of gaseous losses from the soil and from animal excreta. These extra links in the N cycle are shown on the right-hand sector.

on clay and loam than on sandy soils, and on soils derived from basic rather than from igneous rocks. Climate effects can also be important. Waterlogging inhibits the release of soluble nutrients, and dry soil conditions restrict the rate of uptake. Soil-water status and pH also exert a direct effect upon the botanical composition of the sward, waterlogging and acid conditions giving rise

*Table 12.1   Plant nutrients in a grazing system. Quantities of nitrogen, phosphorus and potassium in soil, herbage and animal components of the system, and rates of movement of cycling nutrients**

	Nitrogen (N)	Phosphorus (P)	Potassium (K)
Quantity of nutrient (kg/ha): in			
Soil	10 000	2 000	45 000
Herbage	200	40	300
Animals	20	10	10
Quantity of nutrient (kg per ha per year):			
Released by mineralisation in the soil	70	10	40
Fixed by rhizobia	150	—	—
Added in fertilizer	120	30	40
Taken up by sward	180	20	140
Eaten by animals	150	17	120
Returned in animal excreta	140	15	110
Lost to the atmosphere	50	—	—
Lost to drainage	30	—	1
Immobilized in the soil	150	20	20

* These values illustrate the relative magnitude of the quantities of the major plant nutrients in soil, sward and animal components of a grazing system and the flows which occur between these components over the course of the year. They are approximate values for an intensive beef-cattle or sheep-grazing system on a mixed grass/clover sward.

to populations of plants of low production potential and frequently low nutritive value.

Waterlogging should be corrected by attention to drainage, and acid soil conditions by liming. There are essential preconditions for high grassland production. Inadequate drainage can also have a serious impact on herbage and animal production because of the risk of sward and soil damage from the hooves of grazing animals, particularly in wet weather.

Excreta return and nutrient cycling

Of the major plant nutrients consumed in grazed herbage, 80–90 per cent of the N, 90–95 per cent of the P and almost all of the K are excreted again in faeces or urine, and only small amounts are retained in animal tissues or removed as milk (Table 12.1). Thus, recycling in excreta is an important component of the economy of these nutrients in grazing systems. Most of the K is excreted in urine and almost all of the P in faeces, whereas N is excreted in roughly equal proportions in urine and faeces. The nutrients in faeces are largely in organic compounds and will only become available to the plant as these compounds are broken down in the soil, but the N and K in urine are readily available for uptake by plants. Nutrients returning to the soil in the form of litter from ungrazed herbage become available for plant use much more slowly because of the slow rate of breakdown of undigested plant material. Thus, although the amount of a given nutrient in the soil may in fact be greater under inefficient than under efficient grazing management, the rate at which it moves (amount per unit area per unit time) round the cycle soil – plant – animal will be lower. It follows that efficient herbage utilization will improve the efficiency of use of the plant nutrients in a grazing system at any level of input of fertilizer nutrients. This is particularly important in relation to the transfer of fixed N from clover to grass plants in a mixed grass/clover sward.

The recycling of plant nutrients via the animal has one major drawback, however, which has to do with the fact that dung and urine are deposited in discrete patches on limited areas of sward. Thus the distribution of nutrients in excreta is at best uneven and, in enclosures which are large enough, there will be progressive concentrations of nutrients in some areas and depletion of soil stores in the rest of the enclosure. Probably only 1–2 per cent of a grazed area may be covered by dung in the course of a year, and a somewhat larger proportion by urine, the proportions increasing with stocking rate. The proportion of the area actually affected by the N and K in excreta will be greater than these estimates suggest because of mobility of nutrients in the soil. However, the high concentrations of nutrients in the vicinity of dung and urine may limit the efficiency with which they are used and, at least in the case of the most soluble and readily available constituents in urine, can result in substantial direct losses to leaching or volatilization. The patchy distribution of urine and faeces also contributes directly to variation in herbage growth and this effect is exacerbated by the way in which grazing animals tend to avoid herbage contaminated by faeces.

Fertilizer use

Nitrogen is usually the plant nutrient of most importance in the UK and a distinction is often drawn between the basal requirements for P and K needed to ensure vigorous herbage growth and the production response to a range of N inputs (Fig. 12.3). The distinction is rather artificial because production responses can be demonstrated to all three nutrients, and interactions between their effects are often important. In countries like New Zealand which are heavily dependent upon clover for the supply of N in the sward, production responses to phosphate fertilizers are of major importance.

The general shape of the herbage production response to nitrogenous fertilizer takes the form shown in Fig. 12.3, the rate of increase in herbage production per kilogram of N applied falling from about 30 kg dry matter (DM) at low levels of N use to zero at high levels of N input. In cutting trials, maximum herbage production is regularly achieved only at N inputs in excess of 500 kg/ha, and herbage production often increases at an almost constant rate up to inputs of about 300 kg/ha (Fig. 12.3). In any particular circumstances the incremental response will be determined by the input of N from all sources, including fertilizer (Fig. 12.2), and by the direct effects of climate and sward management on herbage production. For example, the fertilizer N input giving a herbage production response of 10 kg DM per kilogram N (often used in the UK as an indication of the marginal economic response) has varied from 260 to 530 kg N at different experimental sites in the UK.

Fixation of N from the atmosphere by the rhizobia growing in association with the roots of clover plants in a mixed sward containing 20–30 per cent by weight of clover is of the order of 150 kg/year in the UK, and 180–190 kg in the warmer climate of New Zealand. This contribution of clover to the N economy of the sward is reflected in the substantially higher herbage production of mixed swards than of all-grass swards at low N inputs, and the correspondingly lower response in herbage production to increasing fertilizer N use (Fig. 12.3). The clover content of a mixed sward will normally decline with increasing fertilizer N input because of competition from the grasses, but herbage production from a mixed sward with a good clover content is likely to exceed that from an all-grass sward up to levels of N use in excess of 200 kg/year. However, clover growth is unreliable from year to year so the average contribution of clover to herbage production will usually be lower than 150 kg N per year.

Estimates of herbage production under cutting management

Figure 12.3   *Nitrogen inputs and herbage production on (a) all grass and (b) mixed grass/clover swards under cutting management.*

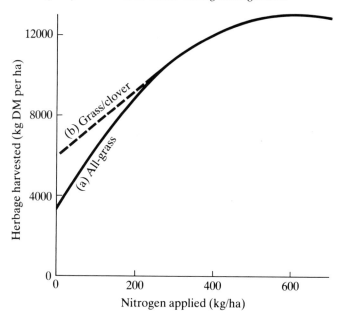

Curve (a) is a typical production response curve to applied N in all-grass swards in a recent national trial, but there were substantial differences between centres in the level of herbage production at any given level of N input (see Ch. 19). Also shown (b) is an average response curve for a mixed grass–clover sward with initially a clover content of 20–30 per cent. Production from mixed swards at low N input is unpredictable, however, as a consequence of year-to-year variations in clover content.

The responses shown here refer to cut swards. Responses under grazing and cutting management are compared in Fig. 12.4.

provide an incomplete answer for decisions about N inputs to grazing systems. Herbage production responses should be greater under grazing than under cutting management at equivalent levels of N input, and the effect of clover on herbage production will also be greater, because more N is recycled via animal excreta (Fig. 12.4). However, responses at high N inputs to grazing systems may be limited by falling efficiency of herbage utilization. Responses under cutting and grazing treatments are shown in

Figure 12.4   *Nitrogen inputs and herbage production under cutting and grazing management. From Frame, J. (1975) Occasional Symposium No. 8, British Grassland Society, pp. 39–49.*

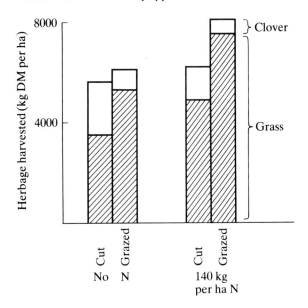

These results refer to mixed swards of perennial ryegrass and white clover cut or grazed at monthly intervals. The N recycled in excreta increased herbage production and also reduced the proportion of the clover in the sward at each level of N input.

Fig. 12.4. It cannot be emphasized too strongly that the key to the effective use of fertilizer N in grazing systems is the efficient utilization of herbage grown (Fig. 12.5).

Where grazing is efficient, each extra kilogram of N should increase output by 10 litres of milk or 1 kg of live-weight gain, whereas the cost of 1 kg of N is roughly equivalent to only 3 litres of milk and less than 0.5 kg of live weight on a finished lamb or cattle beast at present-day UK prices. The arithmetic is not as simple as that, however, because of the need to take into account the capital costs of extra animals and services to utilize the extra herbage. As a rule of thumb, the economic limits to fertilizer N use under efficient grazing management are in excess of 300 kg/ha for milk production and 200 kg/ha for beef and sheep production.

Figure 12.5   The relationship between fertilizer N use and cow grazing days in a dairying enterprise under efficient grazing management.

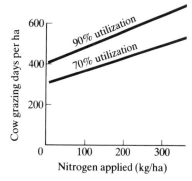

This is an illustration of the relationship between N inputs and the number of cow grazing days per hectare in a dairying enterprise if the herbage grown is efficiently utilized. The effects of grazing management on utilization efficiency were discussed in Chapters 5 and 10.

Livestock grazing days as a measure of production are considered in Chapter 19. Over a 180-day grazing season 450 cow grazing days equate to an average stocking rate of 2.5 cows/ha. Here a good grass/clover sward with a herbage production of 6700 kg of DM per hectare at zero N input is assumed.

Farmers may need to take other factors into account, including the increasing risks of ground-water contamination from high levels of N use, and average levels of N use in grazing systems are much lower. There is no reason why individual producers should not work out production responses for their own conditions and standards of management over a number of years.

Generally speaking, the herbage production response to N input is directly proportional to the rate of herbage production of the sward at the time, so the response would be expected to be greater in spring than in summer or autumn. However, high levels of N use in the spring may have deleterious effects on the sward, and the indications are that total herbage production over the season is affected to only a limited extent by marked variations in the pattern of N application within a season. There are substantial management advantages to be gained from patterns of N use which help to limit the seasonal disparities which frequently exist between rates of herbage production and animal requirements, and a limited increase in herbage production in autumn or late winter may have a far greater impact on the performance of an animal production system than would a greater increase in herbage production in late spring or summer.

Requirements of P and K should be determined by a regular programme of soil analysis. These two elements may be applied alone, or in association with N in a compound fertilizer once or twice in the season. It is usual to avoid the application of K either early or later in the year because uptake at these times can upset the mineral balance of herbage and increase the risk of inducing hypomagnesaemia in grazing animals.

Within these general limits the ground rules for fertilizer use in the UK are relatively simple. The first application of N in the spring should be made 3–4 weeks before the start of grazing to encourage early grass growth, but there is some risk of applying fertilizer too early and losing much of its value by leaching if growth is prevented by a return to cold, wet conditions. There is no way of predicting the likelihood of this event with certainty – if there were, one of the major problems of grassland management would disappear overnight – but it is possible to take some of the guesswork out of the decision by using one or other of the available indexing systems which are dependent upon measurements of either soil or air temperature. The simplest involves the application of fertilizer when the soil temperature at 10 cm below ground level first reaches 5°C in the spring. More complicated alternatives require a daily record to be kept of soil temperature or air temperature, and the application of fertilizer when the sum of the daily readings of soil temperature from 1 January reaches 100 (T value) or the sum of the mean of daily maximum and minimum air temperatures reaches 200 (T sum).

The extension services now publish information on one or more of these indices as a service to farmers, but it is perfectly easy to set up the necessary equipment on the farm. None of these systems can cope with extreme variations in spring weather, but they all help to make spring fertilizer applications a little more objective.

The sequence of fertilizer applications through the growing season will depend upon the total amount to be applied and the desired pattern of herbage production. There is little point in applying less than 30–40 kg of N per hectare at a single application and, usually, little point in applying fertilizer more frequently than once every 3 weeks. Many livestock farmers would settle for a programme involving the application of between 30 and 60 kg of N every 4–6 weeks, giving a total input of between 120 and 240 kg/ha over a 6 month period, though levels of use in dairy systems are often higher than this. The last application of fertilizer is usually made in late August or early September because the slowing of herbage growth in the autumn and recycling of N in dung and urine over the season will combine to render responses to additional fertilizer beyond that time very low. Fertilizer applications can easily be fitted into systems of rotational grazing management and are best timed to follow immediately after a period of grazing. Fertilizer can normally be applied at any time to a continuously stocked sward with little risk to grazing animals, though there may be exceptions during a long dry spell when the sward is grazed very short and fertilizer granules are exposed on the soil surface.

The requirements for N, P and K will all be increased where a cut for conservation is taken. It would be usual to apply up to 80 kg of N and 40 kg of P and K per hectare in a compound fertilizer when a sward is set up for conservation, and a further 40–60 kg of N and 20 kg P and K per hectare after the cut is taken.

Chapter 13   Animals

The animal resources available to a grazier – groups of animals of different species, age, physiological state and productive potential – can be described in three ways:

1. The demands they make on sward conditions to ensure adequate levels of herbage intake;
2. Their ability to tolerate limited intakes;
3. The seasonal patterns of variation in herbage intake to meet specified production targets.

The objective in this chapter is to discuss animal enterprises in these terms before a consideration of the implications to the management of grassland systems in Chapters 15 and 16. In adopting this approach it is important to relate defined animal 'requirements' to the production characteristics of the grazed sward and its responses to management manipulation, because a major function of management is to maintain a sensible compromise between the current and projected 'requirements' of the animals and the need to maintain the productive potential of the sward. Herbage intake should be considered in terms of a response to varying sward conditions rather than as a need which must be met; this explains the use of 'requirements' in quotation marks. Fortunately, there is scope to vary sward conditions within relatively wide limits with little impact on net herbage production (Ch. 5). This provides the opportunity to vary management to suit particular classes of animal without having to worry too much about consequential effects on the sward.

The needs of different animal classes can to some extent be regarded as complementary, lending a flexibility to management which is not easy to achieve in single-enterprise systems. Attention is concentrated first of all on the needs of particular animal classes. Consideration is then given to some of the potential advantages of grassland systems involving groups of animals with different requirements.

Sward conditions   The sward conditions needed to maintain desired levels of nutrient intake and performance can be defined in terms of both nutritive value (digestibility) and quantity (sward height). Examples for selected animal classes under continuous stocking management are given in Table 13.1. The information cannot be comprehensive because evidence is limited.

Animals of high production potential have higher herbage intakes on any given sward than animals of lower potential. However, they will reach a point of nutrient deficit more quickly as sward conditions become limiting, and subsequently their absolute nutrient deficit will always be greater. This point was illustrated in Fig. 7.8 for cows of different milk yield potential. The same arguments apply to animals at different stages in lactation, or with different growth potential as a consequence of variations in age or genetic potential.

*Table 13.1   Sward conditions required to maintain specified levels of animal performance under continuous stocking management**

Animal class and performance	Sward surface height (cm)	Digestibility of herbage consumed (% OMD)
Dairy cow		
30 litres/day	10+	75–80
15 litres/day	7–9	75–80
Suckler cow, mid lactation	8–10	75–80
Dry cow	5–7	70–75
Beef yearling		
1 kg/day	8–10	75–80
Ewe plus twins, early lactation	7–8	75–80
Dry ewe	3–4	70–75

* The conditions specified relate to continuously stocked swards. Lactating animals are assumed not to have to call on body reserves, but some recovery of body-weight is expected in dry animals. There will usually be some balancing effect between herbage quantity and digestibility, an increase in digestibility reducing the standards for height and vice versa.

These specifications take no account of effects on sward conditions or on herbage production. It is very doubtful whether the sward conditions specified for the 30 litre dairy cow can be maintained for very long under continuous stocking, for example. The need for compromise between sward and animal requirements is considered in Chapter 17.

Generally speaking, sensitivity to variations in the standards of sward management will be a direct function of the productive potential of the animals concerned, but the performance to be expected from any given set of sward conditions will also be influenced to some extent by the previous nutritional history of the animals. For example, at any time in the grazing season animals previously underfed will have a higher nutrient demand and a higher herbage intake relative to current live weight than animals previously well fed. In lactating animals the stimulus to herbage intake resulting from earlier limited nutrition may actually enhance milk production.

Breeding cows and ewes can make use of body reserves of energy and protein to sustain foetal growth or lactation where nutrient intake is limited, so their sensitivity to limiting sward conditions is lower than that of growing animals. Even in breeding adults, however, tolerance of limited intake is a function of the amount of body reserves and the magnitude of the demands of lactation, and is likely to be greater in beef cows than in ewes, and least of all in dairy cows. This buffer effect is not without cost because body reserves lost at one time of the year must be replenished at another stage if production is not to be affected in the long term.

Seasonal patterns of intake

The results summarized in Table 13.1 provide static descriptions of the sward conditions required to ensure specified levels of herbage intake at a point in time for particular classes of livestock, but in all livestock enterprises the intake requirements change over time with changes in the size, physiological state and production potential of the animals concerned. The seasonal patterns of herbage requirement for a selection of grassland enterprises are shown in Fig. 13.1, in comparison with the seasonal curves of herbage production from cut swards shown in Chapter 11.

The animal production enterprises which come closest to matching the seasonal pattern of herbage production are those involving ewes and lambs, but in most cases there are marked discrepancies between the patterns of herbage supply and demand. It is emphasized, however, that the curves of herbage production are derived from cut swards; under grazing management (particularly continuous stocking) the spring peak of herbage production is much less marked (Fig. 5.9). The curves of herbage requirement shown in Fig. 13.1 are idealized, and there

Figure 13.1   Seasonal patterns of variations in the herbage requirements of selected animal enterprises: (a) dairy cows; (b) suckler cows; (c) growing cattle; (d) ewes and lambs.

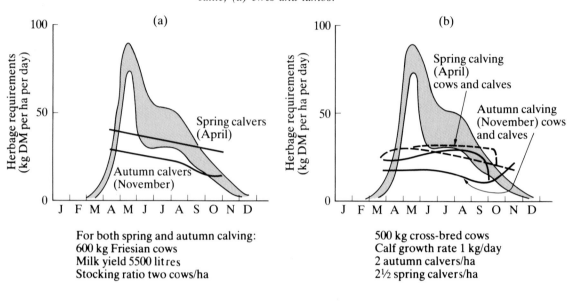

For both spring and autumn calving:
600 kg Friesian cows
Milk yield 5500 litres
Stocking ratio two cows/ha

500 kg cross-bred cows
Calf growth rate 1 kg/day
2 autumn calvers/ha
2½ spring calvers/ha

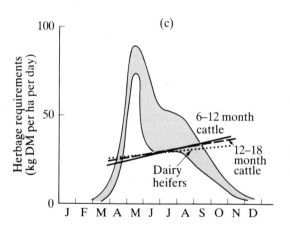

Friesian or cross-bred cattle
Growth rate 1 kg/day (beef cattle)
   or 0.5 kg/day (heifers)
4 cattle 12–18 months, 5 cattle 6–12 months,
   and 5 yearling heifers per ha

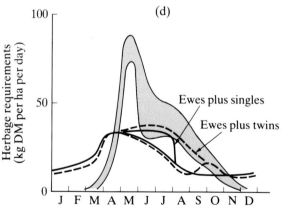

Cross-bred ewes 70 kg live weight
Single lambs fat at weaning, twin
   lambs fattened off grass by October.
12 ewes with twin lambs and 16 ewes
   with single lambs per ha

These are illustrations of seasonal variations in the herbage requirements of grazing animals for several livestock enterprises against the background of the seasonal pattern of herbage production. The curves for herbage production, which relate to swards cut monthly in southern England (see Fig. 5.8), give an indication of the year-to-year variation in the production to be expected at a given time of year. Both the level and pattern of herbage production will be affected by management (Ch. 5) and location (Chs. 15 and 19). Note, however, that the seasonal pattern of herbage production on a farm basis will involve a combination of the curves shown in Figs 5.8 and 5.9.

The stocking rates used are based on an assumed total annual herbage production equivalent to 9000 kg of DM per hectare. (100 000 MJ of ME) and the annual ME requirements shown in Table 13.2, assuming minimal concentrate use for all animal classes except the dairy cow. The specified levels of performance are shown. For simplicity, lactating animals are assumed to maintain weight. Grazed herbage is expected to maintain an organic matter digestibility of about 75 per cent throughout.

is substantial scope for modifying them, particularly in the case of the animal breeding enterprises. In these cases, as has already been indicated, maternal body reserves can be used to help meet nutrient requirements at one time of the year provided that they can be replenished later. The discrepancies themselves are not necessarily a cause for concern. Indeed, in some extensive grazing enterprises it may well not be worth while trying to do anything about them, though this would not normally be the case. Alternative procedures for manipulating the patterns of supply and demand in grazing enterprises are considered in Chapter 16.

Examples of the total annual herbage requirements of representative animal production enterprises in the UK are given in Table 13.2.

Animal populations

Interactions between the individuals making up a population of grazing animals can affect the performance of individuals, and of the population as a whole, in several ways. At its simplest, individuals within a group are in direct competition for food whenever the supply is limited. This is likely to be the case most of the time to a greater or lesser extent in efficient grazing systems. The degree of competition, and the impact of competition on animal performance, will be affected by the mix of animals

*Table 13.2 Annual energy requirements (in MJ of ME) for alternative livestock enterprises in the UK, and provision in terms of grazed grass, conserved forage and concentrates**

	Total energy requirements (MJ ME)	Requirements supplied as:		
		Grazed herbage	Conserved herbage (kg DM)	Concentrate
Dairy cows				
Autumn calving	52 000	2 500	2 000	1 000
Spring calving	52 000	3 000	2 000	500
Suckler cows and calves				
Autumn calving	50 000	2 700	2 000	150
Spring calving	38 000	2 500	1 000	—
Grazing beef cattle				
6–18 months	23 000	1 000	1 000	—
1–2 years	28 000	1 500	750	350
Ewes and lambs				
Singles	6 200	550	50	40
Twins	8 200	700	50	60

* The performance standards assumed are shown in Fig. 13.1. Grazed grass and conserved herbage are both assumed to have an energy value of 11 MJ ME per kg DM. A lower energy value resulting from grazing or cutting at a more advanced stage of maturity would require more DM to meet requirements – or, alternatively, the use of more concentrates.

involved in particular systems. Animals in a group also affect each other as vectors of disease or parasites, the most important effect in the grazing context being related to the transmission and multiplication of gastrointestinal worm parasites. In addition, the tiller population and herbage production potential of a sward may be influenced by the species of grazing animal and by the sward conditions chosen to suit the needs of particular groups of animals.

These observations suggest that grazing enterprises involving combinations of animals differing in species, age or productive state could have advantages over more specialized systems. The advantages might be expected in terms of greater management flexibility and/or in greater output. Many combinations of animal species and classes are possible, and for any given combination the constituent groups may graze together or in some appropriate sequence. Very few of the possible combinations have been studied experimentally, but some of the important aspects of animal combinations are considered in the following sections.

Parasite control   Animals contract and reinforce worm parasite infection by ingesting larvae with the herbage they eat. The infective larvae develop from eggs which are laid by adult worms inhabiting the digestive tract and passed out in the faeces (Fig. 13.2). The larvae have a limited life span, and are susceptible to the drying effects of exposure to sun and wind, and to low winter temperatures. A number of worm species are commonly found in ruminant animals; most, but not all, are host-specific. Their life cycles differ

Figure 13.2   *The life cycle of Haemonchus contortus*, the large stomach worm of the sheep.

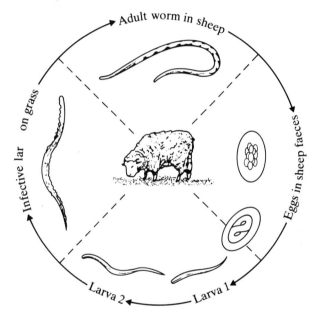

This is an illustration of the life cycle of one of the common worm parasites of sheep. The life cycles of other species may differ in detail, but the principles are the same.

Infective larvae normally develop in 2–4 weeks from eggs deposited in faeces; in the spring they may develop from faeces deposited the previous autumn, but they cannot survive long periods of exposure in the sward. The cycle of infection can be substantially reduced by moving ewes and lambs in the spring to pastures not grazed by sheep in the previous year, and dosing the ewes with an efficient anthelmintic at the time of moving.

in detail, but all have their most serious effects upon young animals which have not developed their own resistance to infection from previous contact. The initial source of infection for young animals comes from the larvae developing from eggs excreted in the faeces by older, contaminated animals, and in most worm species much of the carry-over of infection from year to year comes from worms over-wintering in breeding animals or growing stock. Lambs and calves pick up their initial infection from their dams, and the magnitude of the problem then increases in proportion to the stocking rate of young susceptible animals unless preventive measures are taken. Apart from the obvious effects of overt clinical disease, there is plenty of evidence to show that subclinical disease can significantly depress production.

It was generally believed that managements which involved periodic defoliation followed by periods of rest from grazing would reduce the level of worm infection, for two reasons. A proportion of the infective larvae developing from faeces at one grazing should die before the next grazing, and close defoliation at any one grazing should hasten this process by exposing larvae to desiccation. It is now clear, however, that strategies of this kind have only a limited success in controlling infection, particularly in young animals. The only effective preventive measure is to graze animals on ground virtually freed from infective larvae by preventing grazing by the same animal species in the previous year, and by dosing all animals carrying infection with an efficient drug before they go on to the 'clean' area. This procedure is most effective where animals are dosed when they are moved from winter quarters on to new spring grazing, and is particularly important for breeding ewes and cows. Even this procedure cannot guarantee freedom from infection but it greatly helps to reduce dependence on drugs.

Freedom from infective larvae is most easily achieved on farms where grass forms a break in an arable rotation because cultivation helps to kill residual populations of eggs and larvae, but it is extremely difficult on long-term grassland where most of a farm area is likely to carry grazing animals at some time in the year. In these conditions very close control of grazing management and careful advance planning are necessary.

The fact that the worm populations of sheep and cattle overlap to only a limited extent means that grazing a sward with the two species in alternate years will help to provide the 1-year break needed to allow the parasite population specific to either species to decline to a low level. This is the principle used in the 'clean grazing' system (Fig. 13.3) which for good measure can incorporate a conservation year in a 3-year cycle of use.

This rigid separation of sheep and cattle can introduce difficulties of sward management, particularly in the establishment

Figure 13.3   *The 'clean grazing' system. From Speedy, A. W. (1980) Sheep Production. Science into Practice. Longman.*

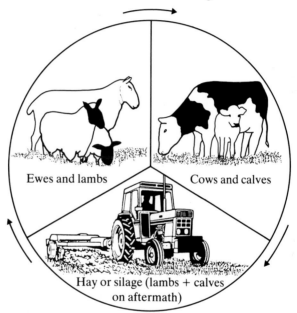

In this system, developed at the East of Scotland College of Agriculture, the sequence of field use in successive years is designed to break the cyclic build-up of worm parasites which tends to occur when young, susceptible animals (lambs and calves)pick up infective larvae developing from faeces deposited by their dams. Sheep are most susceptible to the consequences of worm infestation, but there is relatively little cross-infection between sheep and cattle.

Sheep move in spring on to fields grazed the previous year by cattle, the ewes being dosed before moving. Hay or silage are taken from fields grazed by sheep in the previous year; the aftermaths may then be grazed by weaned lambs or calves, which are themselves dosed before moving on to the clean areas.

phase of new swards but also in the management of established swards. Also, animals reared in worm-free conditions can be very susceptible to infection at a later stage. However, these limitations to management flexibility need to be set against the potential advantages of improved parasite control with minimal recourse to drugs. The alternative is to institute a regular programme of drug therapy to keep levels of infection under control. Sheep appear to be more susceptible than cattle to parasite infection, and the benefits from grazing clean pasture are greater in their case.

Combined grazing of animal species

Grazing cattle and sheep in combination can result in higher levels of animal output per unit area than that achieved from either species alone. The evidence comes from both breeding and fattening enterprises and from different management practices, though in most cases the advantage to mixed stocking is not great. There are several possible explanations for this effect, where it occurs. The presence of grazing sheep helps to prevent loss of tillers and the consequent depression in herbage production under cattle grazing. However, there is no evidence of any advantage for mixed grazing over sheep grazing alone, and no clear indication of a difference in the efficiency of herbage utilization under mixed grazing compared with either cattle or sheep grazing alone under comparable sward conditions. Also, since the worm parasites of cattle and sheep are mostly host-specific, grazing the two animal species together will reduce the stocking rate of animals susceptible to each parasite and would therefore be expected to reduce the level of infestation in both species. This effect is likely to be of greater benefit to sheep than to cattle. Thus any advantage to mixed grazing is likely to depend upon the additive effects of limited advantages to one animal species or the other in different circumstances, and in practice the major benefit may be derived from the greater flexibility of choice in sward management and in the duration of the grazing season as a consequence of working with two animal species rather than one species alone.

Sheep may be able to maintain an adequate level of herbage intake better than cattle under limiting sward conditions, so the cattle are likely to suffer where there is genuine competition with sheep for limited grass resources. This raises the question of the potential value of systems in which sheep follow cattle in sequence, rather than grazing with them, but few of the possible combinations of sheep and cattle in grazing sequences have been examined.

The tendency of goats to graze weed species, and their preference for grasses in mixed grass/legume pastures, offer greater scope for complementary grazing. They have been used successfully for weed control and for enhancing the clover content of pastures in sheep systems, particularly in New Zealand.

Combinations of animals differing in production potential and nutrient requirement

Animals of low current production potential (e.g. mature animals in late lactation or early pregnancy) should be able to tolerate poorer sward conditions or higher grazing pressures than animals of high potential (young growing animals or those in early lactation) whose requirements are not always compatible with the need to achieve close defoliation of the sward (Table 13.1). This has given rise to the view that grazing managements in which more productive animals have first choice of grazing, followed by the less productive animals to clear up residual herbage, may be more efficient than managements in which the two kinds of animals graze separate areas.

Although the performance of the more productive animals may be sustained at a high level in 'leader and follower' systems of this kind, the overall advantages do not often appear to be great enough to justify the extra management effort involved in keeping two separate groups of animals, except perhaps in the specific case of combinations of weaned calves and breeding heifers (Fig. 13.4).

Ewe/lamb and cow/calf combinations

Combinations of adult females and their young can make special demands on management. Sucking lambs and calves do not start to graze substantial amounts of herbage until they are between 4 and 6 weeks old. The rate at which herbage intake subsequently increases, and the age at which it becomes a dominant part of the diet, depend upon the milk yield of the dam and the number of offspring, but lambs and calves are likely to be competing actively for grass with their mothers by the time they are 4 and 12 weeks old respectively. This raises the question of the potential value of managements which provide dam and offspring with access to separate grazing areas.

There are several aspects to this question. The nutrient require-

Figure 13.4 Sequential grazing management for calves and dairy heifers.

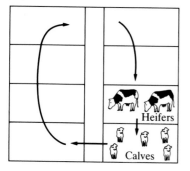

In this system calves move ahead of heifers round a series of paddocks which are grazed down by the heifers and then rested before regrazing. This procedure helps to reduce the transfer of worm parasites to the susceptible calves because they do not have to graze into the base of the sward. It also helps to meet the relatively high grazing requirements of the young animals while providing adequate grazing to meet the more modest requirements of the older stock, and at the same time ensures a high overall grazing efficiency.

ments of the dam decline in late lactation and she can therefore tolerate restricted grazing conditions. There may still be a need to replenish body reserves before the breeding season (in ewes) or the next calving (in cows) but it is usually possible to do this after weaning. The offspring, on the other hand, should normally be kept growing as rapidly as possible over this period and thus require relatively generous grazing conditions. There may therefore be a good case for separating the grazing for dam and offspring, particularly where grass is in short supply, because in this case the young may be penalized by both a low milk intake and a limited herbage intake. This suggestion is reinforced by the increasing risk of worm parasite infestation in young animals which are consuming substantial amounts of herbage from short swards extensively contaminated by infective larvae.

Several procedures have been adopted to allow lambs or calves access to areas of sward which their dams cannot reach ('creep grazing') in an attempt to retain the advantages of a natural milk supply while providing the opportunity for independent grazing activity. In most cases it is also possible to ensure much more generous grazing conditions for the young than for the dam. There is no very convincing evidence to support the view that young ruminants are more selective grazers than adults, but access to generous supplies of young herbage should maintain the herbage intake of young animals at a high level irrespective of any effects on diet selection.

Creep grazing managements have not been very popular in practice, however. This is partly because they have proved to be less effective than expected in augmenting nutrition and controlling parasites, largely as a consequence of the erratic and unpredictable use of the creep areas by young animals, and partly because of the additional management complexities. In many circumstances a more effective solution appears to be to wean the offspring as soon as herbage intake reaches a substantial level and subsequently to manage dam and offspring completely independently. Lambs and calves may be weaned by 6–8 weeks and 16–20 weeks of age if they can subsequently be offered high-quality grazing. This procedure has the dual advantage of allowing the effective use of a relatively small area of a special-purpose crop for the young animals, and better control of parasite infection than is possible when adult animals are present.

Chapter 14 Supplements

Supplementary feeds may be offered to correct specific nutrient deficiencies in grazed herbage, to allow for general qualitative or quantitative limitations in nutrient supply, or to ensure a smooth transition from one feeding regime to another. The supplements used range from simple mineral preparations through conserved forages to complex concentrate mixtures. They can be used as a constant feature of grazing management, or kept in reserve to cope with unexpected grass shortages or nutrient imbalances. The principles are the same in both cases, though the needs for effective monitoring systems are clearly different.

Specific nutrient deficiencies

Herbage will seldom contain essential nutrients in the proportions to provide a fully balanced diet for grazing animals. However, attempts to correct nutrient imbalances by deliberate manipulation of supplement composition are likely to be of limited value except in relation to the use of mineral supplements to control metabolic disorders, of which hypomagnesaemic tetany or grass staggers is of particular importance in the UK. This disorder is the consequence of an inadequate absorption of magnesium from the gut to meet the needs of the animal, sometimes complicated by interference from other chemical constituents of the diet. It is most prevalent in lactating animals with high magnesium requirements and in cold, wet conditions which increase stress on the animal and also tend to depress herbage intake. The tetany is acute, and often fatal unless animals are seen and treated quickly.

The intake of magnesium can be augmented by the use of magnesium-fortified mineral licks or concentrate feeds, or by the use of liquid supplements containing magnesium in solution, some of which may be offered direct to animals in field dispensers and others which are introduced into the drinking water. Alternatively, foliar dusts or sprays containing magnesium can be used to increase intake from the sward. These alternative practices all have their place in particular circumstances, and it is normal to use one or more of them for animals known to be at risk. The main risk periods occur in the spring and autumn, but in some areas may spread over most of the grazing season.

Other mineral deficiencies which may be important in temperate conditions and which are attributable to a greater or lesser extent to limiting concentrations or imbalances in herbage are those associated with calcium, copper, cobalt and selenium. Obvious deficiencies of nitrogen (N) or phosphorus (P) are more likely to occur in tropical than on temperate pastures.

Augmenting nutrient intake

It needs to be said at the outset that there are very few circumstances in which conventional concentrates or forages act as the name 'supplements' suggests, being eaten with no consequent diminution in herbage intake and therefore genuinely supplementing the animal's diet. More often than not their consumption results in some reduction in herbage intake. This is the substitution effect, in which the depression in herbage intake is expressed as a proportion of the amount of alternative food offered (Fig. 14.1). Examination of the theory of the control of herbage intake in grazing animals which was outlined in Chapter 7 will explain why this is so. Herbage intake is influenced as much by behavioural as by nutritional limitations so that, when a readily assimilated source of nutrients is made available in the form of a concentrate, animals are likely to expend less effort in grazing and so reduce herbage intake even where herbage supplies are themselves low enough to limit intake.

The production response of grazing animals to the use of a supplement is likely to be influenced by the characteristics of the grazed sward as well as those of the supplement itself and the way it is used, and by the productive potential of the animals concerned. All these effects are mediated through the substitution which takes place between herbage and supplement.

The degree of substitution appears to be substantial even on hard-grazed swards (Fig. 14.2) presumably because, even though animals are unlikely to be eating to appetite on short or sparse swards, the behavioural responses to the presence of a supplement are likely to be greater in these circumstances than on swards where grazing conditions are easier. This means that a supplement will not necessarily be more effective in improving animal performance when herbage is in short supply than when it is not.

Figure 14.1 *Supplementary feeds: supplementation and substitution effects.*

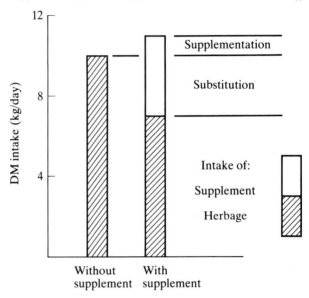

This example illustrates the effect of feeding 4 kg DM of a concentrate or cereal to a grazing beef animal eating 10 kg of herbage DM.

Intake of herbage is depressed to 7 kg of DM, so the substitution effect is

$$\frac{10-7}{4} \times 100 = 75 \text{ per cent}$$

Total DM intake increases to 11 kg, so the supplementation effect is

$$\frac{11-10}{4} \times 100 = 25 \text{ per cent}$$

This is a theoretical example, but the actual response in herbage intake to the introduction of supplementary concentrates in grazing conditions is quite likely to be of this order (see Figs 14.2 and 14.3). The responses shown are measured in terms of DM; effects on the intake of digestible nutrients will depend upon the nutritive value of herbage and supplement.

Substitution is likely to be directly affected by the nutrient concentration in the herbage grazed, particularly when a concentrate is fed (Fig. 14.3). This is because a supplement of high nutrient concentration is likely to enhance the efficiency of rumen fermentation in animals eating a low-quality forage, but the addition of the same feed to herbage already containing substantial amounts

Figure 14.2 *Sward height and feed substitution in lactating ewes. From Milne,*
J. A., Maxwell, T. J. and Souter, W. G. (1981) Animal Production.
32, 185–95.

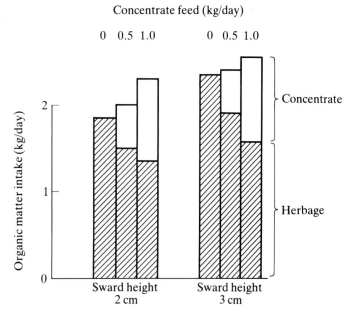

In this example, relating to lactating ewes under continuous stocking
management, the substitution effect of concentrates fed at either 0.5 or
1.0 kg/day was 61 per cent on an organic matter basis on a sward
held at 2 cm, and 87 per cent on a less hard-grazed sward held at
3 cm. Even on these relatively short swards the concentrate acted
largely as a substitute for grazed grass. The substitution rates for
concentrates fed at low (480 g organic matter) and high (960 g) rates
were 66 and 82 per cent respectively.

of readily available energy may actually depress the digestion of
the structural components of the diet.

Small amounts of readily soluble energy and N may improve
the digestion of very poor quality herbage, and in some cases may
actually serve to increase herbage intake. Also, foods containing
proteins which are protected from degradation in the rumen may
stimulate tissue metabolism and herbage intake. In both of these
cases the foods may act as true supplements. With these exceptions, however, there is little evidence to suggest that variations

Figure 14.3 Influence of forage digestibility on the substitution effect of concentrate feeding. Adapted from Holmes, W. (1975) Aspects of the use of energy and of concentrate feeds in grazing management. In Hodgson, J. and Jackson, D. K. (eds), Occasional Symposium No. 8, British Grassland Society, pp. 141–5.

The substitution effect increases from about 35 per cent in forages with a digestibility of 40 per cent to a value greater than 80 per cent in highly digestible forage. The relationship shown is in fact derived from animals given conserved feeds, but the same principles apply to grazing animals.

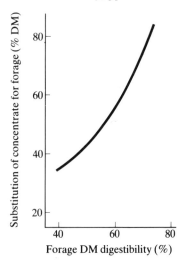

in the physical and nutritional characteristics of feeds will have much influence on the degree of substitution which takes place. The amount of supplement fed will itself influence herbage intake, the substitution rate increasing progressively with increasing supplement intake (Fig. 14.2).

The principles of substitution apply in the same way to the association between the milk and grass components of the diets of lambs and calves, but the substitution rate increases with age as the animal's grazing ability develops (Fig. 14.4). Young animals receiving milk are always likely to grow faster than those which are not, even at high substitution rates, because the efficiencies of digestion and metabolism are much higher for milk than for herbage nutrients.

These considerations help to explain why responses in animal performance to the use of supplements are usually low, except where herbage quality is very poor or where the productive potential of the animals concerned is very high. Examples of measured production responses to the feeding of supplements to grazing animals are given in Table 14.1, together with indications of the levels of responses needed to break even at current feed and product costs in the UK.

A distinction needs to be drawn between the immediate responses to be expected to the feeding of a supplement (Table 14.1) and the longer-term effects once the supplement has been withdrawn. Long-term effects can be complex, and depend in part upon the class of animal considered. In housed dairy cows, for example, the full-lactation response in milk yield to the feeding of concentrates in early lactation may be between three and five times as great as the immediate effect of the concentrate upon milk yield. The effects of concentrate feeding during the winter upon milk yield in the succeeding grazing season are very small, however, and the long-term effects of a temporary feed shortage during grazing upon milk yield may also be relatively small. Young growing animals may show no long-term effects from a

Figure 14.4 Change with age in the substitution of milk for forage in growing calves.

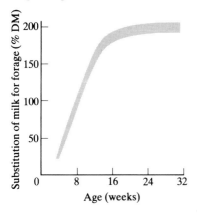

The substitution of milk for forage in milk-fed calves increases with age to reach a plateau level of about 200 per cent on a DM basis by the time the animals are 16 weeks old. Substitution on the basis of digestible or metabolizable energy will be less than 100 per cent however, because of the very high digestibility of milk solids. The change with age reflects the greater ability of older calves to respond to limiting milk intake by eating more grass.

Table 14.1 Normal production responses to the feeding of supplementary concentrates to grazing animals*

	Production response per kg of concentrate	Cost per kg of concentrate relative to value per unit of product (UK prices)
Dairy cows (litres milk)	0.1–1.0	1.06
Beef cattle (kg weight gain)	0.05–0.2	0.1
Sheep (kg lamb gain)	0–0.03	0.1

* Values in the second column are calculated as the cost of barley (pence per kg) expressed as a proportion of the value of animal product (pence per litre of milk or kg of live weight). The production response in the first column needs to exceed the cost/price ratio in the second column for there to be the chance of an economic response to the feeding of concentrates at grass. The cost/price ratio would be lower, and the chance of supplementation being economically justified even lower, if the cost of a compound concentrate had been used in the calculations.

Corrections for differences in gut fill between supplemented and unsupplemented beef animals may improve the estimated production responses a little.

temporary shortage of feed, even though growth is checked at the time. The consequences of a check of this sort will depend upon its severity, and therefore the time taken to recover from it, and the normal life span of the animals concerned. They are more likely to be serious in a lamb with a productive life of 5 or 6 months, for instance, than in a calf with a life of 2 years.

Transitional phases

Despite the above reservations about the production responses to be expected from general supplements, it would normally be considered to be good management to ensure smooth transition from winter feeding to grazing, and back again. This is achieved by gradually tapering off the feeding of winter rations over the first 2 or 3 weeks after animals go out to graze, and by offering some concentrates or conserved forage for a similar period of time before housing in the autumn. The actual benefits of this practice are not easy to demonstrate, particularly where the transition is from a silage-based winter diet to grazed grass or vice versa, but the practice helps to limit the risks of digestive disorder and provides a readily available source of nutrients at the times of year when grass shortages and adverse weather conditions are most likely to limit the nutrient supply from grazed grass.

Supplementation strategy

Grazed herbage is usually a much cheaper form of nutrients than any of the conventional supplementary foods (Table 14.2), so the direct financial benefit to be derived from the use of a supplement depends upon the degree of food substitution which takes place. The above analysis suggests that supplements are often used in circumstances where their impact on animal production is unlikely to be cost-effective, except in the specific case of the correction of mineral deficiencies, and even here it is easy to waste money by over-enthusiastic use of supplements or failure to check on the relative costs of alternative procedures.

However, the overall impact on a grazing system has wider implications than this. The need to assess the long-term effects on animal production of a relatively short period of supplementation – and to recognize that these effects will not necessarily be advantageous – has already been mentioned. Feed substitution may result in a worthwhile saving of grass at a time when herbage growth rates are critically low, irrespective of whether or not any improvement in animal performance is gained, and so can have

Table 14.2   The relative costs of a unit of ME in alternative grass and cereal feeds for ruminants (UK prices)

	Relative cost per unit of ME
Grazed grass	100
Silage	150–200
Hay	170–250
Home-grown cereals	500–550
Purchased compound	650–700

a substantial impact on the subsequent growth potential of the sward. Also, production responses will usually be better on a unit area basis if stocking rates are increased to take account of the herbage-sparing effect of feeding a supplement (Table 14.3). However, in this case the economic analysis will need to take into account the capital costs of any extra livestock required. Perhaps most important of all, the strategic planning of a reserve of supplementary feed will often provide the greater management flexibility and confidence which encourages higher stocking rates and more efficient land use whether or not the supplement is used.

Despite these qualifications, the conclusion must be that the *routine* use of concentrate supplements is a relatively expensive way of maintaining performance in grazing animals in comparison to management options which either grow more grass or encourage the more efficient use of what is grown.

Against this background, if a supplement has to be used at all the choice is best made on the basis of least cost. It is possible that supplements which can be left out for continuous access, like feed blocks or fodder roots, will interfere less with grazing activity and may thus depress herbage intake less than conventional forms of supplement which involve more disturbance for the same nutrient supply, though there is no clear evidence that this is so. Continuous-access supplements are often more convenient to use, but convenience must be balanced against cost. In most cases the use of free-choice supplements of silage, hay or straw is unlikely

Table 14.3 *The effect of supplementary barley on live weight gain per animal and per ha from grazing steer calves**

Level of supplementation (kg of barley DM)	0.6	1.0
Live weight gain (kg/kg of barley DM)		
(a) per animal	0.12	0.05
(b) per ha	0.21	0.24

* These results relate to a study in which the effect of supplementary barley in reducing the herbage intake of individual animals was taken account of by introducing more animals to maintain similar sward conditions to unsupplemented animals. In these circumstances the response in terms of total live weight gain per ha was better than the response per individual animal.

to produce more than marginal benefits to animal performance. However, consumption of these supplements can provide an early warning of developing grass shortages and they can provide a valuable degree of flexibility in intensive grazing systems. The practical aspects of supplement use are considered in Chapter 15.

Chapter 15   Seasonality of herbage supply and feed requirements

The discrepancies between the seasonal patterns of herbage supply and demand were illustrated in Fig. 13.2. Some animal production enterprises come closer than others to matching the typical pattern of herbage production, but in all cases there is likely to be a greater or lesser degree of imbalance. The pattern of herbage production is itself influenced by regional variations in climate. In the south and east of the British Isles, for instance, production in midsummer may be severely depressed by drought; further north and at higher altitude the period of active growth is curtailed because of lower temperatures but growth is less likely to be affected by drought. Seasonal growth patterns for contrasting environments are illustrated in Fig. 15.1.

The implications to grazing management of seasonal disparities in herbage supply and demand have been touched on several times in earlier chapters. In this chapter attention is concentrated on the practical ways in which the discrepancies can be reduced. The alternative procedures include:

1. The use of forage crops with complementary growth patterns.
2. The accumulation of herbage surplus to requirements at one time of year for use in times of shortage, either *in situ* or after storage.
3. The use of supplementary foods brought in from elsewhere.

4. The exploitation of animals' body reserves as an additional source of nutrients at times of feed shortage.

In practice it would be usual to make use of most if not all of these options in a farming enterprise, but decisions about the alternatives are not always easy to make on an objective basis.

Figure 15.1   Seasonal patterns of herbage production in grass swards in different environments.

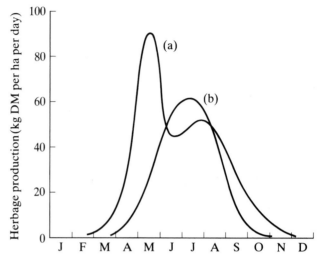

Curve (a) relates to a perennial ryegrass sward in the Thames Valley in southern England, curve (b) to a similar sward at an altitude of 350 m on the Cheviot Hills on the border between England and Scotland. In each case the swards were cut at approximately monthly intervals and received liberal dressings of fertilizer N.

Some decisions are essentially strategic, and concerned with pre-dictable and usually substantial discrepancies between supply and demand at particular times of the year. Others inevitably involve contingency plans to provide flexible responses to unpredictable but short-term discrepancies which are often associated with the vagaries of climate. In practice the two overlap, and both are considered here.

The assumption is often made that matching of supply and demand is a desirable objective. This may be true in general terms but it is not necessarily the case, particularly in the more extensive grazing systems where the cost benefits are likely to be low. It is possible to define the sward conditions which should optimize the balance between sward and animal for substantial periods of the grazing season, but it is not always easy to demonstrate the production penalties which might ensue follow-ing planned departures from the ideal for limited periods of time.

Similarly, it is possible to define the nutrient requirements of grazing animals on the basis of predetermined production targets, but the effects on animal performance of temporary failure to meet these requirements are not easy to establish. There is no very clear evidence that production penalties are necessarily associated with a degree of flexibility of growth patterns in grazing animals, or that wide fluctuations in the body reserves of breeding animals have any substantial impact on either reproduction or lactation so long as recovery is possible at some stage in the annual production cycle.

Thus there is much scope for accumulating nutrients at one time of the year in the form of either herbage reserves or body reserves in order to use them later, provided that the needs to recover sward condition and to replenish depleted body reserves are recognized. These options in themselves provide a great deal of flexibility in most grassland enterprises, particularly where they involve combinations of vegetation and/or livestock resources.

Patterns of herbage production

Some smoothing of the more extreme seasonal variation in herbage production can be achieved by the use of plant species or varieties with complementary growth patterns. Legumes have a slower spring growth and more sustained summer production than the grasses, for example. The ability of some plant species to grow earlier in the spring (e.g. Italian ryegrass and tall fescue) or later in the autumn (e.g. rape and kale) than the grasses in widespread use is particularly valuable. The use of crops like these will help to extend the periods of active growth in the spring and autumn, and the use of drought-resistant species like lucerne will reduce the risk of depressed summer production in some areas. However, with these exceptions, the scope for varying the seasonal pattern of herbage production by judicious choice of plant material is limited. Most of these special crops have specific management requirements which limit the flexibility with which they can be used, and plant species with different growth patterns cannot readily be incorporated into mixtures for general use. Thus, the use of this strategy to reduce seasonal variations in herbage production is confined largely to circumstances in which limited areas of special-purpose crops can be integrated with larger areas of general-purpose swards. A spring reseed will also maintain production through the summer months so long as there are no drought limitations.

Some diversion of fertilizer nitrogen (N) use from the spring to the summer and autumn will also help to reduce the disparity between rates of herbage production at these times of the year. The response to N is proportional to the growth potential of the sward at the time of application so that any diversion of the use of fertilizer until late in the season will reduce the amount of herbage produced per unit of N applied, but this may be counterbalanced by the value of extra herbage grown at a time when feed supplies fall short of demand. Early N application is vital to the encouragement of early grass growth, so the scope for reducing early spring application is limited. It is also possible to limit the spring flush of growth to some extent by hard grazing to prevent stem elongation in reproductive tillers.

Herbage accumulation and conservation

All of the management options considered in the preceding section can help to reduce the seasonal variation in rates of herbage production but, ultimately, their effect is limited to the period of the year when temperatures are high enough to sustain reasonable growth rates. The alternative is to accumulate herbage during periods of surplus and to conserve it, either *in situ* or in store, for use in periods of shortage. The deliberate accumulation of herbage during the summer and autumn for grazing in winter is now seldom practised in the UK, but is an integral part of grassland management in a more favourable climate in New Zealand. A less extreme approach is the accumulation of the regrowth following a conservation cut in the early summer for grazing in the later summer and early autumn. These practices may result in inefficient use of the accumulated herbage and high senescence losses. Their value in a management system will depend upon their influence upon animal performance and the availability and cost of alternative feed supplies. The value of the brassica crops for winter feeding has much to do with the way in which they retain their nutritive value in adverse climatic conditions.

Cutting and storing herbage from the peak period of growth as either hay or silage for feeding out during the winter months is the universal practice throughout temperate Europe, and is an integral part of grassland management. It can be seen as a means of manipulating stocking rate on grazed areas, thus increasing the flexibility of sward control. However, because preliminary judgements have to be made about the proportion of the total area to be taken out for conservation, and because these areas must then be isolated from grazing for some weeks, the control can only be approximate. Further, the accumulation of herbage on areas set aside for conservation is likely to reduce tiller populations and future regrowth potential. On all of these counts silage is a better form of conservation than hay because it allows a more flexible response to changing climatic conditions and a shorter period of herbage accumulation, in addition to the advantages of a more digestible product and a greater tolerance of adverse weather.

The relative requirements of herbage for grazing and conservation depend upon the livestock enterprise concerned (Table 15.1). In the UK the amount of conserved herbage fed can vary from almost 50 per cent of the total forage requirements in the case of dairy enterprises based on autumn-calving cows and intensive beef enterprises based on autumn-born calves, down to less than 10 per cent in the case of sheep enterprises which do not involve early lambing. The duration of the winter feeding

Table 15.1   The conservation requirements of alternative grassland enterprises*

Enterprise	Conservation (% of total herbage DM)
Dairy cows	
Autumn calving	45
Spring calving	40
Suckler cows and calves	
Autumn calving	43
Spring calving	30
Grazing beef cattle, autumn born	
Finish at 18 months	50
Finish at 2 years	33
Ewes and lambs	
Singles	8
Twins	7

* The requirements for conserved herbage are expressed here as a percentage of the total annual herbage DM requirements for each enterprise, assuming similar ME values for grazed and conserved herbage. Where the energy value of conserved herbage is lower than that of grazed herbage, as is often the case, the conservation requirements would increase. The values shown in this table are based on calculations from Table 13.2, and relate to UK conditions.

Figure 15.2   *The incorporation of conservation areas into grassland enterprises: (a) dairying; (b) intensive beef production; (c) beef fattening; (d) lamb production.*

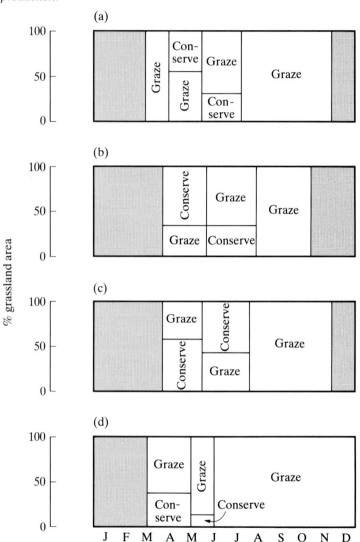

These examples illustrate the integration of grazing and conservation in four systems of animal production from grass. In each case the balance between the areas devoted to grazing and conservation reflects the balance between summer and winter feed requirements, and the *timing of conservation reflects, at least in part, the seasonal pattern of feed requirement for the animals concerned (see Table 15.1).*

The sheded sections indicate periods of winter housing.

Variations in the duration of the grazing season are explained partly by climatic differences and also by differences in the sensitivity of systems to adverse weather conditions in the autumn, winter and spring.

period itself may vary from 3 months in south-west England to 6 months in northern Scotland and this will also influence the demand for conserved feed. In New Zealand most livestock farmers rely on grazed pasture as the main feed supply for virtually the whole year. Examples of the incorporation of conservation into grassland enterprises in the UK are shown in Fig. 15.2.

In general terms there are advantages to be gained from the effective integration of grazing and cutting managements over the course of the year. Grazing helps to maintain tiller populations and long-term sward viability, whereas cutting for conservation helps to reduce the variability which can develop under grazing management, by removing the adverse effects of dung deposition; improves the uniformity of subsequent grazing activity; and helps to control the build-up of worm parasite populations. Where conservation requirements are high, grazing management is likely to be very strongly influenced by the demands of the conservation programme, and where they are low the area for conservation may hardly be adequate to provide management flexibility. However, it is important to retain as much flexibility as possible in the timing and the extent of the conservation programme, and to consider objectively the relative advantages of procedures which safeguard conservation at the expense of grazing, or vice versa. For example, because the milk yield of ewes is very sensitive to variations in herbage mass in the critical early weeks of lactation, a good case can be made for delay in closing up areas for conservation until sward height is adequate to ensure them an adequate level of herbage intake. In conditions of spring grass shortage a decision about closing up for conservation depends upon an assessment of the balance between the cost of purchased winter feed and the cost of reduced lamb growth rate which will be manifest, ultimately, either in a lower realization value or greater total feed costs.

There is no reason to assume that swards initially set up for conservation should not be used instead for grazing if conditions require it, and indeed this may often be a sensible strategy to use even though it requires that an alternative source of feed is found for the succeeding winter. The main requirement is that the herbage should be rationed to ensure efficient utilization. A flexible approach of this kind allows spring stocking rates to be set high enough to ensure effective sward control without the worry of running short of feed in midsummer. This principle is used in the buffer grazing system developed recently by the East of Scotland College of Agriculture for use with growing cattle. In this system, one-third of the designated grazing area is set aside at the start of the grazing season for an early silage cut, but is made available for grazing if the sward height in the main grazed area falls below target. Sward targets for beef cattle are outlined in Chapter 17. If the buffer area is required for grazing before the silage crop is taken, it is advisable to control grazing with an electric fence. After cutting, it can be released for grazing or part of it retained for a second cut as appropriate.

Control of herbage intake and use of body reserves

It is not helpful to consider the nutrient requirements of animals without specifying the levels of production to which the 'requirements' relate. All animals operate on response relationships between nutrient input and performance of the kind illustrated in Chapter 8.9. In many cases the simplest way of dealing with seasonal imbalances between herbage supply and demand may be to allow animals to move, within limits, up and down their response curves. There is more flexibility of operation in some circumstances than in others, but in no case should it necessarily be assumed that it is essential to maintain animals or swards 'on target'. The appropriate approach is to appraise the balance between the financial penalty of any effect of a limitation to herbage intake upon animal performance and the cost of either preventing this limitation or of compensating for it at some future stage.

The maintenance of nutrient intake is clearly more important for some animals (e.g. fattening lambs or cattle) than it is for others (e.g. replacement breeding stock). However, even in the former case some recovery to specified targets is possible if grazing limits can be relaxed following a period of shortage. The effects of short-term limitations of nutrient intake in both growing and lactating animals may be transient, though the magnitude of these effects must clearly be related to the severity and duration of the period of shortage. Pregnant and lactating animals can be expected to call on body reserves to maintain production during periods of restricted nutrient intake, provided that there is the opportunity to recover lost reserves subsequently. There is more scope for flexibility in ewes and suckler cows than in dairy cows, but in all cases there is opportunity to use body reserves to transfer nutrients from times of feed plenty (or cheapness) to times of feed scarcity (or expensiveness). In suckler cows this transfer normally takes the form of the exploitation of body reserves during the winter and their replenishment during the summer, so the scope for making further calls on reserves during the summer period may well be restricted by the need to ensure adequate recovery of body condition before the next winter. In ewes there is often a more straightforward question of the balance between loss of reserves during lactation in the spring, when herbage growth is limited, and recovery in late summer after the lambs are weaned.

There are limits to the use of body reserves in this way, however. Body condition has a direct impact on reproductive performance and lactation in breeding females, and there can be a substantial feed cost to replenishing reserves, particularly where this has to be achieved by the use of supplementary feeds. Body condition scoring has become an established procedure for assessing the body fat reserves of both sheep and cattle, and recommended standards are summarized in Table 15.2.

Deliberate restriction of herbage intake, particularly where this is done to eke out limited herbage supplies, requires strict control of grazing. In these circumstances some form of rationing is important because this ensures a reasonably constant, if limited, herbage supply each day. This is the basis for successful winter grazing management in New Zealand, in which autumn-saved pasture is rationed in 1–3-day blocks to groups of animals, often at the maintenance level of feeding, in order to ensure adequate supplies of pasture for lactating animals in the spring.

Supplementary feeds

The principles of supplementary feeding were considered in Chapter 14 and it was suggested that, under normal conditions, production responses to the routine use of supplements during the main grazing season are likely to be low, especially in meat

Table 15.2   Target condition scores for cattle and sheep*

	Calving or lambing	Lactation (minimum)	Weaning	Mating
Suckler cows				
Autumn calving	3	2	$2\frac{1}{2}$	$2\frac{1}{2}$
Spring calving	$2\frac{1}{2}$	2	3	2
Ewes	$2\frac{1}{2}$	2	$2\frac{1}{2}$	$3\frac{1}{2}$
Dairy cows	$3–3\frac{1}{2}$	$2–2\frac{1}{2}$	3	$2–2\frac{1}{2}$

* Condition scoring provides a subjective assessment on a scale of 1 to 5 of the fat reserves of an animal by handling the loin and tail head regions. The values shown are specific to particular animal classes, and similar values for different classes do not imply similar levels of fatness. Details of the condition scoring procedures are given in many local and regional extension publications.

production systems. Furthermore, the high cost of concentrate feeds and conserved herbage relative to grazed grass means that they are unlikely to be attractive as a means of overcoming predictable periods of feed shortage during the grazing season except in well-defined circumstances.

In sheep systems, the use of supplementary concentrates to augment early spring grazing has a limited impact on lamb growth to weaning, but is likely to have a beneficial effect on the maintenance of ewe body reserves. This is particularly important in the case of thin ewes and in conditions of extreme grass shortage. The value of the herbage-sparing effect of supplements on the growth of spring swards can be substantial and can last well beyond the early phase of growth. In intensive sheep systems autumn grass supplies may often be inadequate for the levels of nutrient intake needed to sustain high ovulation rate and subsequent embryo survival. In these circumstances, too, the tactical use of concentrates to sustain intake at a critical time may often be justified. Levels of concentrate use for ewes should not normally exceed 500–600 g/day in either spring or autumn.

Concentrates may also be used to augment limited herbage supplies in early spring and late autumn in cattle systems, though here there is usually less pressure to turn productive animals out in spring or to continue grazing in autumn when sward conditions are inadequate. In these circumstances concentrates or conserved forages are likely to be used principally at levels up to 1–2 kg/day to provide a gradual change-over from indoor to grazing conditions, and vice versa.

Concentrates are still routinely fed to grazing dairy cows, particularly in the second half of the grazing season, despite much evidence that their use is unlikely to produce a financially worthwhile response in milk yield. High-yielding animals are more likely to be in nutrient deficit than low-yielding animals, particularly in autumn grazing, though high-yielders will eat more grass than low-yielders in any sward conditions. Again the maintenance of body reserves may be a more important function than any direct impact on current milk yield, particularly if reserves lost during the second half of the grazing season have to be replaced during a relatively expensive period of winter feeding. The concentrate feeding scales suggested in Table 15.3 take these practical issues into account, but concentrates should not be used to buffer the effects of inefficient sward management.

The major value of supplementary feeds lies in their flexibility of use and the convenience with which they can be introduced into a grazing system to meet unpredictable feed shortages. Shortages which occur as a consequence of prolonged cold or drought are difficult to deal with in any other way, though even here it is important to have an objective basis for deciding which groups of animals are in greatest need and when to start feeding. The use of concentrate supplements should be linked to the sward targets discussed in Chapter 17.

*Table 15.3 Suggested concentrate feeding scales for grazing dairy cows (kg concentrate per kg milk)**

Grazing conditions	April/May	June–August	September–October
Poor	0.25	0.35	0.45
Moderate	0.15	0.25	0.35
Good	0.05	0.15	0.25

* 'Poor' grazing implies mature herbage and sward height below 7–8 cm (Ch. 17); where sward height is limiting supplementary forage should also be made available.
'Moderate' grazing implies mature herbage or sward height below 7–8 cm.
'Good' grazing implies young herbage of high digestibility, and sward height within target range (Ch. 17). The small amount of concentrate on good grazing during the spring is intended primarily as a carrier for magnesium.

The use of silage or hay as a free-access supplement ('buffer feeding') is now becoming an accepted part of intensive grazing management, particularly for high-performance cattle systems. Used in this way the conserved feeds act as effective buffers against short-term grass shortages during the summer, and quick indicators of such shortages. They also provide a flexible means of smoothing out seasonal fluctuations in feed supply and demand, and help to bolster confidence in systems designed to ensure high efficiency of grassland utilization. Where buffer feeds are used they should be made available on a free-choice basis during the summer and in the autumn once sward height falls below the targets shown in Table 17.1. To be effective, the buffer feeds used need to be kept fresh.

Complementary animal resources

The final option for planning flexibility lies in the deliberate manipulation of the livestock population to control herbage demand. The best example of this approach is the sale of lambs from a ewe flock at weaning in mid season, before the autumn decline in herbage growth. This gives probably the best match of any livestock enterprise to the seasonal pattern of herbage production but it can seriously limit marketing flexibility. In some cases the provision of special crops to provide feed for lamb finishing in the autumn and winter is a more satisfactory alternative. Alternatives for cattle enterprises are less clear-cut because of the longer time-span of the production cycle, but the phased selling of animals from a cattle-finishing enterprise in the late spring and summer is one example. Greater flexibility can be achieved in both sheep and cattle systems by buying in finishing animals to eat off herbage surplus to immediate requirements, but this option is greatly influenced by market constraints. In milk production systems and some breeding enterprises the animal population is more or less static and flexibility must be sought either in terms of the selective limitation of herbage intake for the least sensitive groups of animals like replacement stock or dry animals (examples were given in Ch. 13), or the deliberate over- or under-grazing of some grassland resources in order to preserve others.

It is usually advisable to concentrate on making the most effective use of the best grassland resources and to maintain sward conditions and management objectives on them as close to target as possible, even if this means making less than effective use of the poorer resources. Areas with very specific management requirements, like the special-purpose crops considered in Chapter 11, should have highest priority. This seems obvious but it is not always easy to meet the objective as stated without advance planning. Examples of this kind of decision-making are the initial choice in the spring of areas for summer grazing or conservation, and the allocation of grazing areas for lactating and dry stock. The separation of animal production classes is usually done for convenience of animal management, but it also provides the opportunity for controlling grazing management to meet the differing requirements of different groups of animals. To be fully effective this requires that the most productive stock should be allocated to the best resources, but some flexibility of approach is needed for sward control, if necessary by combining groups of animals. A good example is the New Zealand practice of combining groups of animals into big mobs for rationed grazing during the winter.

The greatest flexibility in the integrated use of grassland resources comes, paradoxically, on farms with a substantial proportion of unimproved pasture. In these circumstances the policy should be to concentrate efforts on providing the best possible grazing on limited areas of improved pasture for animals with the highest nutrient requirements–lactating ewes with twin lambs and young or thin ewes with singles, for example. The nature of the unimproved pasture is usually such that ewes grazing on it with single lambs can readily be used as a flexible source of animals for grazing control in the improved areas, moving limited numbers in and out as sward conditions dictate.

Conclusions

The examples given in this chapter illustrate the range of options for dealing with regular seasonal imbalances in herbage supply and demand. The choice of options will differ markedly in different circumstances, depending upon the particular combination of climate and soil limitations, animal enterprises and farm resources, but in all cases it is necessary to plan and use the options objectively. It is important, for example, to be sure whether the correction of anticipated feed shortages would be achieved most economically by using more fertilizer or by using supplementary feeds, or whether some adjustment of stocking policy would not be more effective than either.

The short-term and unexpected feed shortages which may result from a cold spring or a summer drought, on the other hand, re-quire feeding strategies with a substantial degree of flexibility. Usually these have to be based on a reserve of food either in the form of conserved forage or as concentrates.

Given the importance of conserved forages for winter feeding there is an understandable reluctance to use them as a feed source during the grazing season, but this is not always the most rational approach. Concentrates are almost invariably easier to feed and provide greater management flexibility, but they may often be a relatively expensive form of nutrients.

Chapter 16   Grazing methods

The framework for sward management is set by the planning decisions which influence the overall and seasonal balances between herbage production and demand. Within this framework, the objective of grazing management should be to control plant and animal resources to maintain high overall efficiency in the production system. In this context the condition of the sward itself is much more important to the success of a grazing enterprise than the method of grazing management adopted.

The alternative methods of grazing management are outlined in this chapter in order to distinguish some of their more important characteristics and their potential contribution to grazing systems. Practical aspects of sward control are considered in Chapter 17.

Methods of grazing management (Fig. 16.1) can be divided into those involving **continuous stocking**, in which animals are continuously present on a sward for several weeks or even for a whole season, and those involving **intermittent grazing**, in which an area of grass is grazed down quickly before the animals are moved on to a new area. **Set stocking** is a special case of continuous stocking in which a fixed number of animals remain on a specified area for a prolonged period of time.

Continuous stocking does not imply the continuous defoliation of individual tillers or plants — the results shown in Chapter 5 demonstrate that the intervals between defoliations can vary from 5 days to as long as 3 or 4 weeks — but in this case access to particular areas of sward is not controlled as it is under intermittent grazing.

Intermittent grazing may involve a regular sequence of grazing and rest over a sequence of fields or paddocks (**rotational grazing**) or a much less formalized arrangement. Divisions may be set up on the basis of permanent or temporary fences; the most extreme procedure, in which herbage is rationed on a daily basis using temporary fencing, is **strip grazing**. Rotational grazing manage-

Figure 16.1   Methods of grazing management.
(—) Permanent fencing; (– – –) temporary fencing.

Set stocking

Continuous stocking

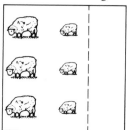

Rotational paddock grazing

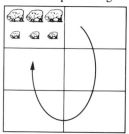

Strip grazing

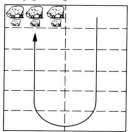

Continuous stocking –
creep grazing

Rotational creep grazing

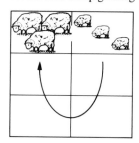

Forage Feeding

This is a diagrammatic illustration of the common alternative methods of grazing management. The characteristics of the alternative procedures are discussed briefly in the text, but it is important to remember that the procedures are means to an end and not ends in themselves. The objective is sward control.

ments can be described in terms of duration of both the period of grazing, which may vary from 1 day to 2 weeks, and the period of recovery from grazing, which will normally be between 2 and four weeks. The sum of the grazing period and the rest period determines the duration of the grazing cycle, the time elapsed between successive defoliations, and the ratio of rest period to grazing period determines the number of fields or paddocks in the system. In the rotational managements the term 'stocking density' is used to describe the number of animals per unit area in a grazed paddock at any point in time, whereas the stocking rate defines the number of animals per unit of the total area available for grazing.

The sequence of use of individual paddocks can be flexible, depending on circumstances, and paddock boundaries may or may not be fixed. These variations do not really affect the principles involved, but they may have a bearing on the ease with which conservation practices can be incorporated into the grazing programme. Any of these management practices can be modified to allow young animals to graze areas of pasture to which their dams are denied access (**creep grazing**).

Zero grazing or fresh forage feeding is strictly not a grazing management at all since it involves the cutting and carting of fresh forage to housed animals, usually on a daily basis. It is mentioned here because it helps to indicate the practical limitations of existing grazing managements, and because it may be contemplated as one of the management tools in a grassland enterprise. **Storage feeding** is a variant in which forage is cut and conserved (usually as silage) before being fed out.

It was generally believed that levels of animal output would be greater under rotational grazing management than under continuous stocking, because it was assumed that control of patterns of defoliation and regrowth would enhance herbage production. However, the evidence now available indicates clearly that variations in grazing management within quite wide limits are likely to have little impact on the amount of herbage produced and consumed per unit area.

The indications are that, at similar stocking rates, meat production per hectare may be 6–7 per cent greater under rotational grazing than under continuous stocking, but milk production only 1–2 per cent greater. There is little to suggest that the difference increases with increasing stocking rate within commercially viable limits. Within rotational managements an increase in the length of the rest period between grazings from 1 week to 3 weeks results in average increases in herbage accumulation or animal production of about 30 per cent. A further increase in the rest period from 2–3 weeks to 4–6 weeks gives only a modest further advantage to production, increasing herbage accumulation by 5 per cent and animal production by 3 per cent on average over a series of trials with meat- and milk-producing animals. These results probably reflect, in part at least, the difficulties of achieving effective herbage utilization in the tall swards which result from a long period of growth.

Thus it seems that there is likely to be little difference between the alternative grazing management strategies in terms of herbage production and animal performance provided that sward management is efficient. There are, however, a number of practical aspects which need to be taken into consideration in deciding which of the alternatives to adopt. In most circumstances continuous stocking and intermittent grazing managements should be regarded as complementary rather than alternative procedures, and used in combination to make efficient use of sward resources.

In many respects continuous stocking is the most effective management for encouraging the high tiller populations which help to ensure sward stability. It provides settled conditions for livestock, and sward changes are relatively slow. This makes for relatively simple sward monitoring programmes. Rotational grazing, on the other hand, requires many more short-term decisions because of the larger number of individual paddocks involved and the relatively rapid changes in sward conditions upon them. In this case it will usually be necessary to monitor conditions both before and after grazing, and to check regrowths, in order to integrate the use of a series of paddocks effectively. Animals tend to be less settled and to exert their own influence on management decisions.

Rotational grazing managements are particularly appropriate to the rationing of access to special-purpose crops (e.g. Italian ryegrass in early spring or the brassica crops for autumn and winter use), many of which may only be suitable for a single grazing, and for rationed grazing of limited feed supplies. Intermittent grazing is also necessary to maintain vigour in forage plants like lucerne and red clover which are sensitive to frequent defoliation. Furthermore, it provides the opportunity for organizing the sequential grazing of groups of animals with complementary functions, examples of which were given in Chapter 13. Rotational grazing managements involve greater costs of fencing, water provision and access roads because of the larger number of subdivisions required, though the costs of fencing and watering, particularly in cattle systems, need not be high.

It is sometimes argued that continuous stocking managements make it difficult to plan field allocations in advance and to react to unexpected climatic variations, and reduce the flexibility of conservation programmes. These objections are not necessarily valid, though some form of intermittent grazing management can help in the forward planning of feed resources and particularly in feed rationing during periods of shortage. These are aspects which can make a substantial contribution to confidence in planning grassland management and, hence, to the efficiency of a grazing system.

Against this background the choice of grazing management is perhaps best made to fit the layout and access routes of a particular farm, the constraints set by other enterprises, and the inclinations of the farmer. The choice should not be influenced by erroneous assumptions about the anticipated effects on herbage and animal production.

Forage feeding procedures result in greater animal output per hectare than conventional grazing managements because they allow more flexibility in herbage growth and harvesting routines and usually give higher efficiency of utilization of the herbage grown. Few reliable comparisons have been made on a long-term basis but, on average, the advantages to forage feeding systems in terms of animal production per hectare have been about 25 per cent. So long as such systems make use of existing winter accommodation and conservation equipment the capital costs are not necessarily high, and there may be advantages in terms of flexibility of farm layout and reduced fencing costs. However, machinery costs tend to be high because of the heavy demands for the regular handling of bulky herbage and animal excreta.

Forage feeding is not widely used as a routine system, but it may offer short-term advantages in dealing with particularly tall swards or special crops, and in allowing the harvesting of herbage under ground conditions which would normally be too wet to allow access to grazing animals. Willingness to use conservation machinery in this way can make a substantial contribution to management flexibility.

Chapter 17 Sward control and grazing management

Levels of herbage production and animal performance are closely related to sward conditions. Sward surface height provides an effective way of summarizing sward condition, particularly under continuous stocking management, and an objective basis for running grazing systems with reproducible results. The procedures for enterprise planning which determine stock numbers and the general balance between herbage production and demand are outlined in Chapter 19. Here the objective is to indicate the ways in which sward height targets can be chosen to suit the requirements of particular production systems, and used as an objective basis for day-to-day management decisions on grassland control in order to adjust for seasonal and short-term fluctuations in herbage growth or feed requirements.

It is not realistic to expect to be able to hold swards close to target at all times, though Chapters 5 and 9 illustrate the consequences of a drift away from target on herbage production and the predictability of animal performance. Once control of a sward is lost, moreover, remedial measures can have serious consequences on animal performance. Management responses to changes in sward height away from target can include adjustments in the use of fertilizers or supplementary feeds, but will often concentrate on adjustments in the balance between areas used for grazing and for conservation. All of these issues have been discussed in general terms in earlier chapters, but must now be linked to sward targets. A conservation strategy which allows for flexible adjustment of grazing areas can create problems, particularly where conservation requirements are a particularly large or particularly small component of the total forage needs of a system. In most cases only a limited proportion of the total conservation areas is likely to be involved, however.

Sward targets | Specifications for the sward conditions needed to ensure high rates of herbage production and utilization are shown in Chapter 5. The relationships between sward height and net herbage production are of general application to swards based on perennial ryegrass and other species with similar prostrate growth habit and high potential tiller populations, though actual levels of herbage production will vary depending upon site, fertilizer use and season of the year. Sward height specifications to suit the needs of different livestock classes are listed in Chapter 13, and these are also of general application over a similar range of sward types. These specifications provide the basis for target sward height recommendations for particular enterprises.

Some of the specifications for animals under continuous stocking management fall within the range of sward height likely to

Table 17.1 Sward targets for grazing management. Sward heights providing a reasonable compromise between sward and animal requirements for a range of livestock enterprises under continuous stocking management*

	Sward surface height (cm)
Dairy cows	
High yielders	8–10
Low yielders	7–9
Finishing beef cattle	7–9
Store cattle	6–8
Suckler cows and calves	7–9
Dry cows	5–7
Ewes	
Early–mid lactation	4–6
Dry	3–4

* These are targets for main season grazing. Suggested seasonal variations are discussed below, and summarized in Table 17.4. It would be very difficult to meet the needs of cows giving more than 25 litres of milk daily without some form of management to ensure that lower yielders clear up residual herbage. Dry cows in late pregnancy would need to have sward targets similar to those for lower-yielding cows. The targets for spring calving suckler cows are adequate to allow body-weight recovery of about 0.5 kg/day, and could be reduced for cows not needing to gain weight.

These targets relate primarily to wards dominated by perennial ryegrass and white clover. Comparable information is not available for other pasture species.

optimize net herbage production, and in these cases sward and animal requirements are quite compatible. This is particularly true for sheep systems. Some of the cattle specifications, however, involve swards carrying too much herbage for proper grazing control, and in these cases some compromise is needed to ensure an adequate balance between the requirements for high animal performance and for efficient herbage utilization. The range of compatibility may be greater under rotational grazing than under continuous stocking, particularly where rotational grazing allows some integration of high-demand and low-demand stock.

The sward conditions which should achieve a reasonable compromise between sward and animal requirement for the main livestock enterprises under continuous stocking manegment are shown in Table 17.1. These specifications should provide general targets for sward management for the main part of the growing season, but alternative target heights can be chosen to meet the needs of specific production systems. Target sward conditions are illustrated in Plates 17.1–17.4. Target conditions for rotational grazing systems are not so well defined; suggested values are given in Table 17.2.

Sward target management: winter and spring

The scope for manipulating rates of herbage production and for changing grazing management varies over the year, the options available being much greater in the main growing season than in the autumn, winter and spring when growth rates are low. In this section the objective is to consider the ways in which grazing management must be adjusted to cope with seasonal changes in herbage production, and the links between management and herbage production in different seasons.

*Table 17.2   Target grazed stubble heights for rotational grazing systems (cm)**

Sheep	4–6
Finishing beef cattle	7–10
Lactating dairy cows	7–10
Store cattle/dry cows	6–8

* These target stubble heights are for 3–4 week rotational managements in which pre-grazing sward heights are 15–30 cm, and also relate to swards dominated by perennial ryegrass and white clover.

Plate 17.1   Target sward conditions for lactating dairy cows.

Plate 17.2   Target sward conditions for spring calving suckler cows.

Plate 17.3   *Target sward conditions for dry cows.*

Plate 17.4   *Target sward conditions for lactating ewes.*

Figure 17.1   Sheep wintering: winter stocking rates and effects upon herbage production in the following year. After Black, W. J. M. (1975) Irish Journal of Agric. Res., 14, 275–84 and 17, 131–40.

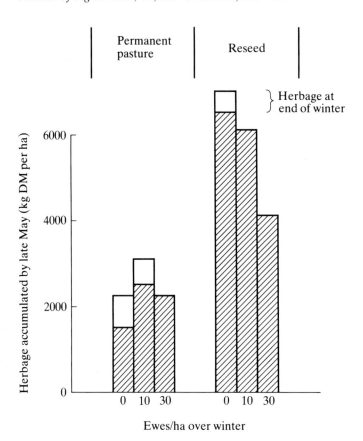

This is an illustration of the effects of sheep stocking rate over winter on herbage production in the following year for a permanent pasture and a new reseed. One treatment was unstocked, and on the others the sheep stocked at 10 or 30 per hectare received silage to appetite in addition to grazed herbage. The stocking rate affected the amount of herbage remaining at the end of the winter, but had little impact on subsequent herbage accumulation (hatched columns) on the permanent pasture. However, herbage mass in early May was reduced by winter stocking. This can be a crucial time for lactating ewes.

The new reseed was more sensitive to winter stocking, probably because of lower tiller density and poorer sward formation, and herbage accumulation was depressed at all stages of the subsequent season.

These results refer to swards on a well-drained soil. On heavier soils or under impeded drainage the effects on the sward would be much more serious. In these trials herbage production on the permanent pasture was affected to only a limited extent by stocking rates as high as 100 ewes/ha; at this stocking rate spring production on the reseed was depressed by between 50 and 75 per cent and total production was also seriously affected.

In most of the UK herbage, growth continues during the winter at a slow rate, providing the basis for limited grazing if soil conditions allow. Rates of herbage growth and senescence over this period are more or less in balance, so new leaf cannot be accumulated on the sward and has to be grazed as it grows. Usually, also, tiller populations tend to fall slowly over the winter. Any ungrazed herbage remaining in the autumn will be lost over the winter, and can contribute to the death of underlying tillers in freezing conditions. Thus it is sensible to graze autumn pastures down to a sward surface height of 2–3 cm, removing as much mature leaf as possible in the process. This grazing is best done with animals with relatively low feed demands, preferably with sheep if there is any risk of sward or soil damage in wet conditions.

Herbage production in the following summer can be depressed by severe defoliation during the winter, particularly if this is accompanied by treading damage (Fig. 17.1). However, maintenance of the specified sward conditions by grazing sheep should have no adverse effects, and may help to maintain tiller populations. A rate of herbage growth averaging 5 kg of dry matter per hectare per day should provide grazing for three ewes per hectare over the winter, soil conditions permitting, but the feed requirements of larger numbers of sheep will need to be met from conserved feed. In areas of heavy or badly drained soil, consideration should be given to the advantages of removing sheep from the fields entirely in order to prevent excessive poaching damage and the consequent loss of tillers resulting in depressed growth in the following season.

In countries like New Zealand where winter temperatures are high enough for continued herbage accumulation, intensive grazing can continue year-round. In these conditions pastures are stocked heavily for short periods of time, often only once during the winter, and grazed to a residual height of 1–2 cm. This practice has no adverse impact on herbage growth potential, and can help the control of weed grasses which are more sensitive to close grazing and treading damage than are perennial ryegrass and white clover.

The rate of herbage growth increases rapidly in early spring from the low and level characteristic of winter conditions, but swards are usually considerably shorter than during the main grazing season and the onset of rapid growth is unpredictable because of variable weather conditions. Ewes in early lactation at this time of the year have particularly high nutrient requirements and their herbage intake can be twice that of barren animals, so they are particularly sensitive to variations in sward conditions. Herbage intake increases rapidly as sward height increases to 4–5 cm under continuous stocking management, and this is reflected in increased lamb growth rates and weight changes in the ewe.

The objective should therefore be to bring spring swards up to target conditions as quickly as possible in order to ensure efficient herbage production and adequate levels of herbage intake to meet the high feed requirements of lactating ewes. Swards which are grazed hard through late winter and into the spring will take longer to reach full efficiency and, if stocking rates are high enough, may never do so. In addition, levels of herbage intake and animal performance are likely to be restricted for longer. The objective is aided by early and generous application of nitrogenous fertilizer to encourage early grass growth. Consideration should also be given to the advantages of continuing to make conserved feeds available until target sward conditions have been attained. It is not sensible to wait until sward height reaches the main season target of 4–5 cm before stocking grazing areas. A more realistic target would be 3–4 cm, on the assumption that rapid growth rates in spring will soon result in an increase in height, even though there may still be the risk of a check to growth in cold conditions.

The substitution effect of concentrates for grazed herbage means that they have a limited effect on lamb performance even on short spring swards, though in these circumstances they do help to limit weight loss in ewes (Fig. 17.2). In the case of particularly thin ewes, this can be of critical importance. The substitution effect also helps to restrict herbage intake, and the

Figure 17.2 *The effects of sward conditions and the use of supplementary concentrates on (a) lamb growth and (b) ewe weight change in early lactation. From Milne, J. A., Maxwell, T. J. and Souter, W. G. (1981) Animal Production, 32, 185–95.*

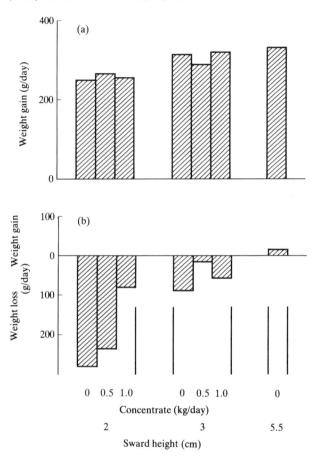

Sward conditions had a greater effect on both ewe weight change and lamb growth than did the use of supplementary concentrates because the concentrates reduced herbage intake even on the short 2 cm sward. The effect of the concentrate would have to be assessed in terms of a saving in ewe body reserves and a saving of herbage at a critical time of the season, rather than in terms of enhanced lamb growth. However, these results apply to ewes in good body condition at the time of lambing; for ewes with poor body reserves the concentrate may have had a more direct effect on lamb growth.

use of supplements at this time of year may be justified simply in allowing the more rapid recovery of sward height towards the critical initial target of 4–5 cm. It should usually be possible to cut out concentrates once sward height exceeds 4 cm.

Similar arguments apply to swards for grazing cattle, though in this case there is seldom the same pressure for the early onset of grazing because of the risk of sward damage on a wet soil and because of the limitations to herbage intake in cattle grazing short swards. In this case the turn-out target height should be 4–6 cm. There is no clear indication that rotational grazing will have any advantages over continuous stocking at this stage of the season. In many respects the advantages should be to a continuous stocking procedure which allows animals to take herbage as it grows, coupled, if necessary, with a limited programme of supplementation to restrict herbage intake until production catches up with demand. In a wet spring a rotational grazing management will concentrate treading damage on limited areas of sward, whereas continuous stocking management will create more limited damage over a wider area. The choice of alternatives – including the extreme solution, keeping animals inside until ground conditions improve – depends very much on the climate and soil of a particular farm, and on farm layout. Concentrate feeding can be discontinued once sward height exceeds 6 cm (8 cm for spring-calving dairy cows).

Sward target management: summer

Herbage will start to accumulate in the sward as growth rates accelerate in the spring, and it will soon be necessary to make decisions about the proportion of the grassland area to close up for conservation, and the timing of closure. This decision is frequently made on the basis of the anticipated need for winter feed, leaving the grazing animals to make the best use they can of the remaining area. This may be a justifiable approach in cases where the requirement for conserved feed is high, and it certainly simplifies the decision-making process. It is usually sensible, however, to make the decision in relation to the likely impact on the performance of the grazing animals. It is also necessary to assess the relative costs of lost performance at the time and of purchased feed for the winter.

Where decisions on conservation are made with the interests of the grazing animals in mind, they need to take into account the current herbage mass on the sward and the anticipated rates of herbage production and consumption per unit area up to the time when the conserved swards can be returned to grazing. The closures can take place virtually as soon as swards reach target conditions because by then the chances of continued rapid growth on the grazed areas are high.

An indication of the stocking rate adjustments needed to correct for changes in sward height during the main grazing season is given in Table 17.3. Adjustments can be made either by adding animals or by taking out a proportion of the grazing area for conservation. Sward height targets should also be used as a basis for determining fence movements in buffer grazing managements, and the start and finish of periods of forage feeding in buffer feeding systems, in each case using the values in Table 17.1 as a guide to restrict grazing or make more feed available.

The practical issues involved in integrating grazing and conservation, and their implications to feed budgeting procedures, will influence management decisions. In most cases the choice between the alternative management procedures for the main grazing season is unlikely to influence sward or animal performance materially – provided that the alternatives can be run

Table 17.3 Stocking rate adjustments to compensate for sward height changes under continuous stocking management*

| | | Change in height over previous week | | |
		Decrease	No change	Increase
Current height	High	0	+10	+20
	On target	−10	0	+10
	Low	−20	−10	0

* The figures indicate the changes in stocking rate (expressed as a percentage of current stocking rate) needed to respond to changes in sward height between successive measurements, taking into account any difference between current sward height and target height. The values shown can be applied to both sheep and cattle systems. These adjustments are intended to keep sward heights close to target over a sequence of successive weekly measurements.

Because of sward variations, estimates of mean sward height are usually only accurate to about 0.5 m, so it is important not to react too quickly to small changes in height. Frequent changes in stocking rate are not often necessary once target sward height has been established in the spring.

efficiently – and the choice can reasonably be made on the basis of management convenience or personal preference. The period of rapid growth in spring is a critical time for grazing management, however. If the stocking rate is set too low at this time herbage will rapidly accumulate, leading to the development of flowering tillers which animals will subsequently be reluctant to graze. This will result in a loss of tillers, with serious consequences to the future productive potential of the sward, and in the nutritive value of the herbage.

Tiller populations will also decline in swards set up for conservation and it is advisable to bring these swards back under grazing management quickly in order to prevent further tiller losses. In particularly dry areas it may be preferable to maintain swards at a greater height than is strictly needed to optimize herbage production and animal performance. This provides something of a feed buffer when growth fails, though swards maintained in a short, leafy condition are if anything less drought-sensitive than taller swards carrying a greater mass of herbage. When growth starts to fail because of shortage of water there is little to be gained by allowing swards to be grazed much below 3 cm because at this level even the limited current growth capability will be reduced and, worse, the future recovery of the sward will be adversely affected. In these circumstances it is likely to be more sensible to make use of part of the conserved feed or supplementary concentrates to reduce the herbage consumption of the grazing animals. Use of areas originally set up for conservation is best handled by rationed grazing to ensure efficient utilization of long herbage and to help to spin out limited feed resources.

Sward target management: autumn

The return to conditions in the autumn where the rate of herbage production fails to match demand introduces a different set of problems. This is of greatest importance in the case of sheep, which usually remain at grass much later in the autumn than cattle, at a time when their feed requirements to sustain good reproductive performance are likely to be high. In these circumstances it may be necessary to accumulate herbage on some areas towards the end of the main growing season in order to have feed reserves for later use. This introduces the risk of high herbage losses, particularly at a time of year when senescence and decomposition rates may be accelerated by wet conditions or frost damage. The consequence may be a decline in the digestibility of the diet which is exacerbated by the need eventually to graze into senescent material at the base of the sward. Also, the nutritive value of live plant material is lower in the autumn than earlier in the year. These factors are likely to result in limitations to nutrient intake and depressed animal performance, and poor efficiency of use of the herbage grown. Production responses to variations in herbage mass or sward height at this time of year are difficult to establish and it seems very likely that the factor exerting the greatest impact on animal performance will be the amount of live leaf per unit area of sward.

Thus the scope for the accumulation and utilization of herbage in the autumn is probably limited, and there seems little justification for accumulating herbage much in excess of 6–8 cm in height for sheep, or 8–10 cm for cattle. Effective utilization of accumulated herbage probably requires some form of rationed feeding, but this in itself is likely to limit intakes.

Where there is a need to maintain levels of animal performance in the autumn in the face of a declining supply of grass, the sward height targets shown in Table 17.1 can be used to determine the time to start feeding supplements. Suggested seasonal variations in sward height targets for sheep and cattle systems are summarized in Table 17.4.

Table 17.4 Seasonal variation in sward height targets for continuous stocking management, taking into account adjustments in spring and autumn*

	Sward surface height (cm)	
	Sheep	Cattle
Winter	3–4	
April	3–5	5–8
May		6–8
June	4–6	
July		
August	6–8	7–10
September	(Dry ewes 3–4)	
October		
November	4–6	

* Graze down to 3–4 cm by December. Timing of spring and autumn changes depends upon location.

Sward problems and restitution

Sward deterioration may occur as a result of patchy grazing, poaching in wet conditions, smothering by dung and urine scorch, and by the loss of tillers, either singly or in clumps. Not all of these effects can be avoided by good grazing management, and the consequences of some of them are difficult to overcome by subsequent manipulation, but the scope for effecting some degree of recovery in damaged swards is considered here. Patchy grazing can occur as a consequence of the patchy distribution of dung and urine or of soil contamination, and in response to the variable distribution of plant species in the sward. The effects will be exacerbated by low grazing pressure and will themselves contribute to poor herbage utilization. Many of these effects, once initiated, can be very persistent.

The avoidance of herbage growing in the vicinity of dung pats will always create a degree of patchiness in a grazed sward. The proportion of the areas left ungrazed can vary from 10 to 45 per cent, depending on the stocking rate. For comparable managements the proportion of the total area left ungrazed at any time may not be very different under cattle grazing and under sheep grazing, though the areas rejected by cattle are more obvious because they are larger and more persistent, and have more herbage on them.

The effects of a dung pat upon herbage rejection may persist for 3–5 months, depending on circumstances, the duration of the effect usually being longer in dry than in wet conditions. This effect, coupled with the seasonal variation in herbage growth rate, means that rejected areas associated with dung pats usually increase to a maximum in midsummer and then decline in the autumn. Attempts to overcome the effects of dung contamination include the preliminary conditioning of animals, treatment of dung pats to disguise their smell, and harrowing to spread the faeces more uniformly. All of these procedures can reduce herbage rejection, though to a limited degree, and it is doubtful whether any of them are of practical value. Grazing control will reduce the adverse effects of dung or soil contamination but cannot eliminate them entirely.

Patchy grazing itself is primarily a consequence of understocking, and will be associated with limited efficiency of herbage utilization. Attempts to improve the uniformity of grazing by topping ungrazed areas are likely to have only a limited impact unless they are accompanied by an increase in stocking rate, or

occur at a time when the herbage growth rate is declining natural-
ly. Otherwise, the sward is likely to return rapidly to the same
condition. In general, patchy grazing and seed-head development
are unlikely to be a problem in swards maintained below 6 cm in
sheep systems or 8–10 cm in cattle systems.

Recovery treatments on under-grazed swards are largely a question of hard grazing or close cutting to remove the accumulated
ungrazed herbage as quickly as possible, allowing light to
penetrate to the base of the sward and stimulate tiller development. Grazing animals are unlikely to clean off a mature sward
of this kind unless they are kept at high stocking rate. Thus,
recovery grazing is best carried out with mature, dry stock with
limited nutrient requirements. Cattle will usually graze more
uniformly than sheep in these circumstances. A trimming cut or
a cut for conservation is the quickest way to achieve the desired
end, but any conserved feed taken from a mature sward will inevitably be of low nutritive value. The effects will only be
temporary unless they are followed by an increase in stocking rate
to improve grazing efficiency, or they coincide with a fall in
herbage growth rate.

Tiller development and sward recovery following corrective
grazing or cutting will be aided by an application of fertilizer
nitrogen, and the increase in tiller population following a return
to efficient grazing will be faster in spring than later in the year.
Continuous heavy stocking with either sheep or cattle is also
likely to have a beneficial effect on swards in which low tiller
populations reflect mismanagement or sward damage in previous
years. In these circumstances recovery to an adequate tiller
population and sward density might be expected within the course
of a grazing season. The excessive loss of tillers as a consequence
of frank over-grazing is not often a problem and, when it occurs,
it is usually associated with particularly dry conditions. Sward
recovery in the same year is likely to be slow. Loss of tillers as
a consequence of inadequate grazing control in spring followed
by over-grazing in summer and autumn is a widespread problem
however, particularly under sheep grazing. Return to a maintained sward surface height of 3–4 cm the following year will
ensure recovery of tiller numbers in most circumstances, but in
extreme cases sward replacement may be necessary.

The loss of tillers under cattle grazing compared with sheep
grazing, and the consequent depression in herbage production,

demonstrate the potential value of the presence of sheep in cattle-grazing systems. This effect is apparent over a full season, but sheep may be particularly useful to tidy up cattle-grazed swards in the autumn.

The production potential of the sward may be adversely affected by direct damage occurring as a consequence of the activities of grazing animals. Damage in this sense covers the smothering of tillers by dung, damage caused to tillers by hoof pressures in dry conditions and to both plants and soil in wet conditions, the scorching effect of high urine concentrations, uprooting of tillers or whole plants, and soil compaction. The magnitude of these effects upon herbage production is difficult to quantify, but in most circumstances is likely to be relatively small, and corrective measures are not often contemplated. The uprooting of tillers (tiller pulling) or whole groups of plants (sod pulling) can reach epidemic proportions on occasion, however.

Tiller pulling in perennial ryegrass is often a consequence of a period of lax grazing resulting in the development of aerial roots with a poor root-hold, and in this case should be avoided by effective grazing management. It is also a characteristic feature of tillers of annual meadow grass, particularly in the late summer and autumn, but this effect is unlikely to have serious consequences. Sod pulling, on the other hand, tends to occur on intensively grazed and heavily fertilized swards. Its cause is not well understood and, in consequence, measures for its prevention and treatment are not reliable.

Hoof damage to sward and soil is usually a feature of wet soils but can occur on almost any soil during the autumn, winter and spring. The only real prevention is to remove animals in wet conditions. This is seldom an option during the main grazing season but it is often possible to control the times of starting grazing in the spring and stopping in the autumn in order to reduce the risks of damage. Where grazing is unavoidable damage is minimized by reducing stocking density, but some farmers prefer to concentrate stock on sacrifice areas in these circumstances. Damage is always likely to be less on short, dense swards than on tall, open swards. Cattle are likely to do more damage than sheep because of their greater weight. Perennial ryegrass is less susceptible to treading damage than other grasses and the legumes, but it is doubtful whether these species differences are important at normal stocking densities.

Compaction of the soil at heavy stocking rates may eventually reduce herbage production, particularly on the heavier soils, as a consequence of reduced soil-pore space and impeded drainage, but this is not often a problem in temperate countries at normal stocking rates. Recovery management is more difficult to contemplate when soils have been extensively damaged or compacted by hoof action. Under these conditions it is advisable to replace the sward, and cultivation will be necessary to restore soil condition.

Chapter 18   Sward monitoring

Routine animal observations are regarded as a normal part of good husbandry, but swards are seldom accorded the same attention as the animals grazing on them. The regular appraisal of sward conditions is an important prerequisite of efficient grazing management and is essential to a management based on the use of sward targets. Management objectivity is also greatly helped by the adoption of an effective grassland recording programme. These two aspects of grassland management are considered in this chapter.

Sward measurements

The sward characteristics most likely to affect herbage and animal production, and therefore of most importance to management, are surface height, herbage mass and density, and leafiness. It has been conventional to make routine measurements of herbage mass in grazing studies but there is increasing evidence that measurements of sward surface height provide better indications of both herbage production and animal performance in particular circumstances, and more consistent patterns of response under different conditions. This is why more emphasis has been given to sward height than to herbage mass measurements in previous chapters.

Sward surface height is conventionally defined as the average height of the uppermost leaves in an undisturbed sward canopy, measured with the simple 'sward stick' shown in Plate 18.1. A reliable estimate of sward height can be made by recording the average height at which the transparent tongue of this device first makes contact with live leaf as it is lowered on to the sward at forty to fifty points while walking across a field. Measurements should be made at random across grazed and ungrazed areas (only avoiding obvious bare patches and areas round gates, troughs and 'camping' sites) and should be recorded to the nearest half-centimetre. The sward height targets described in Chapter 17 are defined in this way.

Plate 18.1 Measuring sward surface height with a sward stick.

Sward height measurements can also be made with a ruler (Plate 18.2) or a graduated walking stick held at arms length, but the sward stick helps to take some of the guesswork out of measurements and avoids parallax errors. A scale marked on a farm boot can provide a rough guide to sward height but this procedure, and eye estimates, are not accurate enough to use as a basis for management responses to maintain target sward heights.

Herbage mass is measured by cutting a known area of sward with hand shears or powered clippers and weighing the dried herbage. It is more laborious to measure mass than height, but the exercise is a useful one for anyone wishing to learn more about sward structure and morphology, and a knowledge of herbage mass is needed for feed budgeting (Ch. 19). It is convenient to use a wooden or metal quadrat of known dimensions to control the area to be cut. In grazed swards it is advisable to make the quadrats relatively long and narrow (Plate 18.3), and it is helpful to adopt a size which makes it easy to multiply up to hectare units.

It has been usual in grazing studies to cut samples as close to ground level as possible (Plate 18.3), and all the herbage mass values quoted in this book are based on ground-level measurements. However, there is always an element of subjective judgement in cutting and collecting samples, and the possibility of variation in sampling efficiency should always be borne in mind when making comparisons between estimates from different centres. Small areas cut in this way will normally recover quite quickly, but should be avoided in later sampling. Generally ten to twelve quadrats would be required, scattered at random over a field, for a reasonably reliable estimate of herbage mass. Samples should be dried in an oven overnight at 80–100 °C. Use of higher temperatures will char the herbage. The samples can be weighed on an accurate kitchen scale before multiplying up to estimate herbage mass in kilograms per hectare. For anyone wishing to take the process further, estimates of mean herbage bulk density are simply derived by dividing herbage mass by sward surface height.

When samples are cut to ground level it is difficult to avoid contamination with soil. In grassland experiments this can be allowed for by estimating the ash content of herbage samples by burning off all the organic material and expressing the results on an organic matter (i.e. ash-free) basis. This is not normally

Plate 18.3 *Estimation of herbage mass from cut quadrats.*

Plate 18.2 *Measuring sward surface height with a ruler.*

feasible on the farm because high temperatures are required for efficient combustion, but most of the soil contamination can be removed by washing herbage samples on a sieve before they are dried.

The grass meters (Plate 18.4) which are basically a metal plate sliding on a central rod, measure a combination of height and density: They have been used primarily as a means of predicting herbage mass, but the relationship between mass and plate height can vary substantially between swards and over seasons, so they need to be used with care over a range of swards. They do have the advantage of being almost as quick and easy to use as a ruler, and their main value may in fact come to lie in their use for straightforward estimates of sward height on continuously stocked swards. All of the plate meters compress the sward to some extent, and they are not appropriate for use with the sward targets set out in Chapter 17. Electronic probes which measure changes in capacitance related to changes in herbage mass are now coming into use. They, like the plate meters, depend upon the development of a prediction equation to estimate herbage mass from a set of meter readings.

Estimates of leafiness depend at present upon the hand separation of samples of herbage cut from the field. The normal

Plate 18.5   *Sward components: a sample of herbage separated into grass seed head (left), dead grass leaf (centre top), stem and sheath (centre bottom), live grass leaf (bottom right) and live clover leaf and petiole (top right).*

Plate 18.4 A grass meter.

procedure is to divide the samples into live and dead components, and to separate leaf, stem and seed heads (Plate 18.5). The proportion of live leaf in a sward is often surprisingly low. Clover leaf, petiole and stolon can also be sorted.

This procedure adds substantially to the value of simple measurements of height and mass because of the importance of leaf to both herbage production and intake but it is laborious.

All of these procedures provide an effective check on sward

conditions and an objective basis for making management decisions. With practice it is possible to make reasonably reliable visual assessments of herbage mass and sward height (see Plates 18.6–18.8) and it is well worth while acquiring the expertise to do this, if only to provide a basis for discussing grassland topics with neighbours. However, visual assessments need to be regularly checked against actual measurements because it is easy for 'drift' to occur even with experienced observers. There are particular risks in trying to make visual assessments across a series of swards of contrasting species compositions or tiller density and, as already indicated, such assessments are not sufficiently accurate to detect the minor sward changes which give advanced warning of the need for management adjustments.

Within a defined system of management sward height and herbage mass tend to vary together, though the height/mass ratio changes from spring reproductive swards to autumn vegetative swards, and this point needs to be watched if one parameter is to be predicted from the other. When comparisons are to be made between different swards (when comparing notes with a neighbour, for instance, or comparing fields within a farm which have been managed differently) it is advisable to try to make estimates of both height and mass.

Plate 18.6   *Too short! An over-grazed sward with too little leaf. Surface height 2 cm.*

Plate 18.7   Just right for sheep. A continuously stocked sward 4–5 cm tall.

Plate 18.8   Too tall! An under-grazed sward showing seed-head development and an accumulation of dead leaf. Surface height 8–9 cm.

Variations in leafiness are linked closely to variations in height, particularly in continuously stocked swards, but these associations should not be relied upon. For example, a sward being grazed down after a period of lax grazing is likely to produce a largely leafless stubble whereas, at the same mass and height, a sward growing away from a period of hard grazing will have a high leaf content.

Grassland recording

The keen grassland manager will always be interested in the output from his fields and his farm. Measurements can be made – and are made – in terms of milk or meat output, but on this basis it is difficult to make comparisons between different kinds of product, and between fields carrying different proportions of productive and unproductive stock or different animal species or classes. Also, comparisons based on physical output do not easily take into account the contribution which supplementary foods might make to animal performance or the value of conserved herbage taken off a field.

Two alternative recording procedures can be used to overcome these difficulties. One involves the use of standard values to convert individuals in the main animal classes to standard 'animal units', and to record output in terms of the number of livestock units per hectare and the duration of the period of use of a field. The result is expressed as 'livestock unit grazing days' or LUGD. Allowance can be made, if necessary, for any supplements used or conserved herbage removed. The standard units adopted are necessarily somewhat arbitrary, and there have been minor variations in the conversion factors used in different schemes, but the procedure is relatively simple to use. In Europe the standard unit is normally taken to be a dairy cow. In New Zealand it is a breeding ewe. An example is given in Table 18.1.

A procedure which is more flexible but a little more complex relies on estimates of the energy requirements of populations of animals with known levels of production. It takes into account the maintenance requirements of the animals as well as the requirements for production, and adjustments can also be made for feed inputs or conserved herbage in energy terms. The standard estimates of animal requirements in terms of metabolizable energy (ME) provide the basis for the calculations, and output is expressed in terms of joules of ME per hectare or, more conveniently, gigajoules ($1GJ = 1\,000\,000$ J or 1000 MJ) to limit the

Table 18.1   Grassland recording: livestock unit grazing days (LUGDs)

(a) Unit values

The standard LUGD equates to the daily herbage consumption of a dairy cow weighing 500 kg and yielding 3640 litres of milk. Other livestock classes are related to this standard on the basis of an assumed relationship between live weight and herbage intake. For example:

Holstein or Friesian dairy cow	= 1.0 LU
Cattle under 11 months	= 0.25 LU
Cattle 11–20 months	= 0.5 LU
Spring calving suckler cow and calf	= 1.2 LU
Weaned autumn-born calf	= 0.4 LU
Breeding ewe 55–68 kg	= 0.13 LU
(add 0.01 for each 25% lambing percentage)	
Weaned lambs	= 0.04 LU

This is a selection of values; the full list is more extensive.

(b) Calculations

LUGDs can be calculated for individual fields, particular enterprises or the whole farm. In each case the procedure is to calculate

$$\text{LUGD} = \frac{\text{Number of animals} \times \text{LU equivalent} \times \text{days grazing}}{\text{hectares}}$$

It will usually be necessary to break down the grazing season into appropriate periods to allow for changes in stocking rate. The following example illustrates the calculations for a 10 ha field in a dairy enterprise which was used only for grazing.

March–April $\dfrac{20 \text{ cows} \times 1.0 \times 30}{10} = 60$

April–end May $\dfrac{40 \text{ cows} \times 1.0 \times 45}{10} = 180$

June–July $\dfrac{30 \text{ cows} \times 1.0 \times 55}{10} = 165$

August–October $\dfrac{20 \text{ cows} \times 1.0 \times 100}{10} = 200$

November $\dfrac{10 \text{ cows} \times 1.0 \times 30}{10} = 30$

TOTAL   = 635 LUGD

The grazing season stocking rate in this example is

$$\frac{\text{Total LUGD}}{\text{Total days}} = \frac{635}{260} = 2.44 \text{ LU per ha}$$

and in this case there was no need to make allowance for any conserved herbage taken off the area. Estimates of output, particularly from dairy farms, can be substantially higher than this.

number of zeros involved. This provides an estimate of the output of utilized metabolizable energy (UME) from a field or a farm. An example is given in Table 18.2.

Recording schemes using one or other of these approaches are operated by several statutory and commercial agencies and can readily be adopted on a farm basis, particularly with the aid of

---

Table 18.2   Grassland recording: utilized metabolizable energy (UME)

(a) *Values*

The UME system allows greater flexibility of calculation than the LUGD system because it can take into account variations in milk yield and weight change, as well as fine adjustment for differences in animal live weight. It does, however, involve more tedious calculations, and adjustments are still made for supplementary foods on the basis of assumed nutritive value.

(b) *Calculations*

As an example, assume that the cows used in the calculation of LUDG in Table 18.1 were March calvers and were the standard LU cow (i.e. weighing 500 kg and giving 3640 litres of milk in a lactation) – say 3500 litres by the end of the grazing season in November. Assume, too, that no concentrates were fed except for 2 kg/day in November.

UME per cow per day (MJ) = $8.3 + 0.091W + 4.94Y$
where W = live weight in kilos; Y = milk yield in kilos.

For short periods of time allowance should be made for weight loss or gain. In this case assume that cows are roughly the same weight at the end as at the beginning of the grazing season, so no allowance is necessary. Then UME per cow over the grazing season of 260 days is

$(8.3 \times 260) + (0.091 \times 500 \times 260) + (4.94 \times 3500) = 31\,278$ MJ
Less value for concentrates at 11.5 MJ/kg
$(2 \times 30 \times 11.5) = 690$ MJ
$31\,278 - 690 = 30\,588$ MJ/cow

The energy requirements for pregnancy are normally allowed for in the last few months before calving, but in this case can reasonably be ignored.

Grazing season stocking rate (from Table 18.1) is 2.44 cows/ha
The UME output is
$30\,588 \times 2.44 = 74\,635$ MJ/ha
$= 74.6$ GJ/ha

Levels of UME output can be in excess of 100 GJ/ha for efficient grassland systems.

modern computer technology. Of the two the UME system is the more flexible and is now the basis adopted for national recording schemes in the UK. In New Zealand, where there is much less reliance on conservation and feed supplements, the simpler stock unit system is preferred.

Chapter 19 Enterprise planning and feed budgeting

Efficient enterprise planning and forward budgeting of feed supplies are essential prerequisites of effective grassland management. Both planning and budgeting depend upon a combination of reasonably objective estimates of herbage production and consumption over time and, where appropriate, of existing herbage reserves. Although the information available for making some of these estimates is not yet as good as it should be, the calculations involved provide a solid basis for management decisions. Every farmer goes through the exercise in deciding on the number of animals to carry on the farm or to put on a given field, but the assessments are often qualitative in nature and there is room for much more formalized planning than this. Detailed budgeting is particularly important where stocking rates are high and herbage is efficiently utilized – in other words, where there is least slack in the system.

Enterprise planning provides the framework for a farming business and budgeting provides the basis for control and manipulation once a business is in being. The two procedures make use of essentially the same kind of information, but forward budgeting requires a more detailed approach and involves much more response to developing conditions than does enterprise planning, so it is convenient to consider them separately. Attention is concentrated here on feed budgeting, but it is recognized that planning decisions will normally be heavily influenced by the physical and financial constraints of individual farms which may be quite unrelated to feed supplies.

Enterprise planning

A decision on the basic stocking rate appropriate to a particular enterprise requires estimates of the expected annual herbage production for local conditions of soil and climate and the anticipated level of fertilizer use, and estimates of the annual herbage requirements of the expected mix of livestock classes. Estimates of herbage production throughout the UK show local variations of more than 50 per cent about the mean value. A general indication of fertilizer responses is given in Chapter 12, but the initial decisions about fertilizer use should be based on local experience. The predictions of herbage requirements depend to some extent upon anticipated levels of animal performance and assumptions about the use of non-forage feeds, but the requirements shown in Table 13.2 provide a reasonable basis for planning.

A sample calculation of a projected stocking rate is shown in Table 19.1. In most livestock rearing and finishing enterprises decisions about stocking rate and the timing of animal purchases and sales are interdependent so that, for example, a sheep enterprise involving the sale of weaned lambs can carry more breeding ewes than one in which lambs are retained for fattening. It will often be helpful to consider summer and winter phases separately, having gone through the calculation on a full-year basis, in order to anticipate the balance of requirements for grazing and conservation.

The estimates of herbage production used in Table 19.1 are average values and do not take into account the effects of year-to-year variations in climatic conditions. The degree of risk to be accepted in pitching stocking rate on estimates of herbage production above or below the mean is a matter of personal choice, and will be influenced in part by an individual's willingness to buy in feed in times of serious shortage. In a normal run of years, herbage production in the UK is likely to vary by 10–20 per cent on either side of the mean values quoted, with greatest variation in the drier areas of the country; in exceptionally dry years herbage production may fall below the mean by as much as 50 per cent.

The herbage 'requirements' outlined in Chapter 13 should also be treated sensibly, particularly in the case of adult breeding stock where substantial variations in nutrient intake during the year and in the rate of depletion and repletion of body reserves can be accommodated with little impact on performance. Over the course of a year this flexibility may make little difference to feed budgets, but it can have a substantial effect over short periods of time.

Table 19.1   Enterprise planning: calculation of potential stocking rate for a sheep enterprise. Example farm in N. England

(a) Projected annual mean herbage production at 150 kg of N per ha is
8500 kg of DM per ha
From Table 13.2, the annual herbage requirements of a medium-weight (60–70 kg) ewe and her lambs (assuming 160% weaning) is
690 kg of DM
Projected stocking rate is
$$\frac{8500}{690} = 12 \text{ ewes/ha}$$
Since these are estimates of net herbage production from monthly cuts, it should not be necessary to make any allowance for herbage losses during grazing. In a normal run of years the range in herbage production in the example area is 10–20% either side of the mean. This is unlikely to be of great consequence for a sheep enterprise, but in some areas and for some enterprises it may be necessary to adjust stocking rate downwards to allow for a risk factor.

(b) For a flock in which replacements are reared it is necessary to allow for the requirements of the young females. Assume 25% replacement rate, ewes lambing for the first time at 2 years. Then requirements for a (ewe plus followers) unit are
$$\frac{4 \text{ ewes} + 1 \text{ yearling (weaning to first mating)}}{4}$$
$$= \frac{(4 \times 690) + (1 \times 300)}{4}$$
$$= 765 \text{ kg DM}$$
Then overall stocking rate for the enterprise is
$$\frac{8500}{765} = 11 \text{ ewes/ha at 150 kg N}$$

(c) For a sheep system the long grazing season and the relatively small requirements for conserved feed (Table 13.2) mean that there is not much point in making separate calculations for the winter and summer seasons.

For the conservation period assume a conservation crop of 2500 kg DM per ha over 6 weeks. At a conserved herbage allowance of 50 kg DM per ewe (Table 13.2), conservation requirements at 12 ewes/ha = 600 kg. The percentage of the total area needed to meet this requirement is
$$\frac{600}{2500} = 24\%$$
Over this period the *grazing* stocking rates would be 15 ewes/ha. Note, however that these calculations are only planning projections; the objective (Ch. 15) would still be to base conservation decision on the management needs of the grazing area in any year.

Feed resource allocation

Given an established framework within which to operate, budgeting procedures can be used to plan the allocation of feed resources to particular groups of animals over the whole or part of a grazing season, the division between grazing and conservation requirements and, in the short term, the control of stocking on particular swards. Feed budgeting is the term used for these procedures in New Zealand, where they have probably been applied more widely than elsewhere.

In the spring and summer, when the rate of herbage production is likely to exceed current requirements, the emphasis in feed budgeting will normally be on the manipulation of grazing stock and the balance between grazing and conservation to control sward conditions. In the autumn and winter, when the reverse is the case, emphasis will be placed on the use of grazing control to ration limited herbage supplies in the most effective manner to groups of animals with different nutrient requirements. The calculations for forward feed budgeting require detailed information on existing feed stocks and anticipated rates of herbage production, together with estimates of the feed requirements of groups of animals differing in age and stage of production, and, where necessary, a sharp awareness of the priorities for the allocation of limited feed resources between them and the scope for using additional feeds.

It has to be accepted that the information on which to base these calculations is incomplete. In the UK, information on seasonal patterns of herbage production is confined to a very few locations and relates mainly to cut rather than grazed swards. New Zealand information is more comprehensive. Also, the information on feed requirements is derived mainly from feeding standards based on experiments with housed animals and does not take into account the influence of sward conditions on voluntary herbage intake.

Swards should carry forward a limited residue to support subsequent growth; in other words, estimates of current herbage mass do not represent a reserve which can be entirely consumed. It is necessary to correct these estimates for target levels of residual herbage which will be expected to vary during the year, and to be higher during the growing season than in the winter (Fig. 19.1). Also, the residual herbage mass at the end of a grazing period (and the herbage mass maintained under continuous stocking) should be higher for productive than for non-productive

Figure 19.1   Variation over the year in target levels of (a) herbage mass under continuous stocking, and (b) residual herbage mass under rotation grazing.

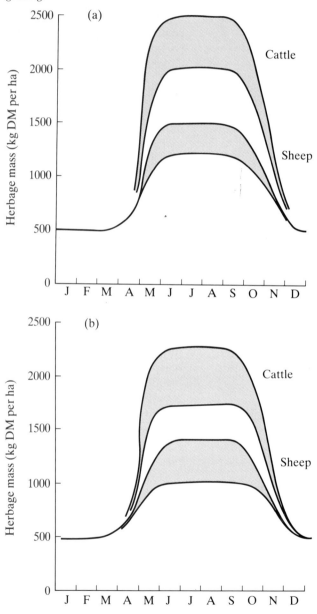

The values shown are based on the sward height targets given in Chapter 17, assuming normal sward conditions, and relate to estimates of herbage mass made to ground level. In each case a range of values is shown for both cattle and sheep during the main grazing season, allowing for variation in the level of animal production. Ideally, sheep and cattle swards should both return to a low herbage mass during the winter, but it is difficult to achieve this without the use of sheep.

For rotational grazing managements (b) individual paddocks may be grazed down in the autumn, or the same result achieved by opening up paddocks to general grazing.

animals. There is no essential difference between the calculations appropriate to continuous stocking and intermittent grazing managements; the practical difference lies in the degree to which limited quantities of herbage can be rationed over time and control exercised over the herbage intake of particular groups of animals.

Examples of feed budget calculations appropriate to a beef herd in the spring and a sheep flock in the summer are shown in Tables 19.2 and 19.3. It is emphasized that the calculations are examples only, and that the information on which they are based is not as good as it could and should be, but the examples serve to illustrate the potential value of feed budgeting in management control and to emphasize the areas within which better information is required. The calculations shown are very laborious in longhand, but can be done easily with modern computing facilities. The budgets shown are on an enterprise basis, but in some cases individual field budgets may be necessary.

Decisions about management strategies arise directly out of these budget calculations. For example, calculations in the spring will indicate the area which should be taken out for conservation in order to maintain the desired sward conditions on grazed areas. If these calculations imply a shortfall in the amount of conserved feed it will be necessary to decide between the options of restricting grazing to release more area for conservation (and the priorities for applying this restriction), of increasing fertilizer inputs to boost herbage production, or of purchasing feed to augment farm supplies. Later in the year the decisions are more likely to have to do with rival claims of growing lambs and of ewes recovering from the effects of lactation for limited areas of

Table 19.2   Feed budgeting for a spring-calving suckler herd: May–June period

---

Background

100 ha grass in ten fields of 10 ha

200 spring calving (March) cows

190 calves (95%); half calves sold in autumn, the rest (mainly heifers) kept for finishing off grass and turned out at 350 kg LW with a projected growth rate of 1 kg/day

Stocking rate 2 cows plus 1 yearling per ha

Nitrogen use 200 kg/ha

Predictions of feed requirements from feeding standards, assuming herbage with an ME value of 11 MJ/kg DM and herbage production from Fig. 11.2

Calculations

(a) May

Feed requirements for cows in early lactation, allowing weight gain of 0.5 kg/day:

14 kg DM × 200 = 2800 kg DM per day

Herbage production = 75 kg DM per ha per day

Area for cows:

$$\frac{2800}{75} = 37 \text{ ha (4 fields)}$$

Feed requirements for calves:

7 kg DM × 95 = 665 kg DM per day

Area for calves:

$$\frac{665}{75} = 9 \text{ ha (1 field)}$$

Area surplus to grazing requirements = 50 ha

50 × 3.5 tonnes DM = 175 tonnes silage DM in early June

Some early grazing probably available in April, assuming reasonable soil conditions, and best utilized by cows

(b) June

Feed requirements for cows as in May; for calves:

8 kg × 95 = 760 kg DM per day

Herbage production = 55 kg DM per ha per day

Area for cows:

$$\frac{2800}{55} = 51 \text{ ha (5 fields)}$$

Area for calves:

$$\frac{760}{55} = 14 \text{ ha } (1\tfrac{1}{2} \text{ fields})$$

Area potentially available for second silage cut = 36 ha

36 × 2 tonnes DM = 72 tonnes silage DM in July

(c) Projected silage total

The projected silage total (175 + 72 = 147 tonnes DM) should be just sufficient to meet the needs of cows and weaned calves over the winter, assuming 1 tonne DM per cow and 0.5 tonne per calf, and herbage growth rates through July and August should be enough to meet requirements. However, heifer calves should be finishing from June onwards, indicating the likelihood of herbage surplus to requirements in late summer and autumn. Consider reducing N input except on silage area, and consider increase in stock numbers for following season. Choice between more cows or higher proportion of calves retained depends upon financial assessment

Table 19.3 Feed budgeting for a grassland sheep flock in July and August, following a conservation cut

Background

30 ha grass in six fields of 5 ha

500 medium-weight cross-bred ewes with 800 lambs (160%)

Stocking rate 16.6 ewes/ha

Nitrogen use 150 kg/ha

Two fields cut for silage mid June

Grazed fields close to target at 1200–1800 kg DM per ha

Ewes to be weaned at the end of July

Predictions of feed requirements from feeding standards, assuming
   herbage with an ME value of 11 MJ/kg DM, and herbage
   production from Fig. 11.2

Calculations

(a) *July*

Feed requirements for ewes in late lactation and their lambs, now
   eating substantial amounts of grass themselves:

3 kg DM × 500 ewes = 1500 kg DM per day

Herbage production:

48 kg DM × 30 ha = 1440 kg DM per day

Thus the feed requirements will just about be met, so long as silage
   aftermaths can be brought into use by the beginning of July

(b) *August*

After weaning, feed requirements are as follows: Ewes at
maintenance only:

0.75 kg DM × 500 = 375 kg DM per day

Lambs growing at 200 g/day:

1.2 kg DM × 800 = 945 kg DM per day

Predicted herbage production 45 kg DM per ha per day:

Ewes require $\dfrac{375}{45}$ = 8.3 ha

Lambs require $\dfrac{945}{45}$ = 21 ha

Ewes on two fields (= 10 ha)

Lambs on four fields (= 20 ha); use silage aftermaths and the best swards from main grazing area

Herbage supply and demand are pretty well in balance over this period However, no provision has been made to cover the rapid decline in herbage production in September and October by starting to accumulate feed on part of the farm. This will be particularly important if ewes need to recover body reserves lost in early lactation before they are mated. Herbage demand can be reduced by selling lambs during August; the number to be sold, and the need to consider selling some unfinished, will be determined by these considerations.

Note: At an N input of 150 kg/ha the use of herbage production estimates from Fig. 11.2 is probably rather optimistic.

new swards or conservation aftermath; with the need to protect other areas from grazing in order to accumulate herbage for autumn grazing; and with the most appropriate procedures for rationing grass or special-purpose crops in the early winter.

All of these options can be budgeted in financial as well as in physical terms, but the basic requirement in each case is an objective appraisal of existing herbage reserves and of anticipated production.

Chapter 20   Conclusions

Grassland systems are often considered to be relatively inefficient farming enterprises when judged on the basis of the wide disparity between average levels of production and achievable targets; and it is frequently suggested that the attainment of greater efficiency depends upon the development of simple 'blueprint' systems which can be readily applied on farms. However, this argument appears to be based on unjustifiable assumptions about the stability of both the climatic variables and the fiscal policies influencing grassland production. What is required, rather, is a set of objective decision rules which grassland farmers can use in enterprise planning and in management control, based on an understanding of the forces which maintain the coherence of grazing systems and the opportunities for controlling them to advantage. In the context of grazing management, understanding does not come from the manipulation of arbitrary variables like stocking rate or rotation length. It depends upon a proper appreciation of:

(a) the influence of sward conditions on herbage production and utilization and on animal performance, which together define the management criteria for achieving particular production objectives, and

(b) the scope for adjusting plant and animal populations, and the balance between forage supply and demand in both the short and long term, in order to meet these criteria.

This is why a substantial part of this book has been devoted to explaining the principles influencing the growth and utilization of grazed plants, and the herbage intake of grazing animals. The sward targets specified for particular grassland enterprises appear to be of general application in temperate climates and provide an objective basis for grazing management decisions, though more research is needed to define the extent to which they apply to plant species differing in growth habit. However, the choice of targets and the procedures for achieving them must depend upon the resources and objectives of individual enterprises. In the later sections of the book the factors which are likely to be important in determining management strategy have been outlined, and some examples of planning options illustrated, in order to provide guidelines for on-farm decisions.

It would be idle to pretend that the limited evidence from detailed grazing studies removes all the uncertainty from grazing management decisions, but there is now enough solid evidence to provide a basis for rationalizing the intuitive nature of many current decisions. The major requirement now is for a body of on-farm information to extend the base of the existing experimental evidence and the inferences that can be drawn from it.

Further reading

Holmes, W. (1980) *Grass: Its Production and Utilization*. The British Grassland Society. Blackwell Scientific Publications, Oxford.

Holmes, C. W. and Wilson, G. F. (1984) *Milk Production from Pasture*. Butterworths NZ Ltd.

Leaver, J. D. (1983) *Milk Production: Science and Practice*. Longman, London and New York.

Nicol, A. M. (1987) *Feeding Livestock on Pasture*. New Zealand Society of Animal Production Occasional Publication No. 10.

Robinson, J. J., Russel, A. J. F., Treacher, T. T. and Kilkenny, J. B. (1983) *Feeding the Ewe* (2nd edn). Meat and Livestock Commission, Bletchley.

Simpson, K. (1983) *Soil*. Longman, London and New York.

Speedy, A. W. (1980) *Sheep Production: Science into Practice*. Longman, London and New York.

Index